Summary

Archaeology is a major factor in construction and development and an estimated £150m is spent by developers on archaeology in the UK each year. As most clients and developers are aware, archaeological remains are treated as a material consideration in the planning process. However, archaeology is often underestimated as a business risk. So it is often not considered early enough in the feasibility and design stages of projects, leading to unexpected and unplanned consequences. Equally, opportunities to add value to a project by integrating aspects of the historic environment into the final design, generating community benefits and positive publicity may be underestimated, or missed out altogether.

Across the UK the legislation and planning advice relating to archaeology is prolific. There are numerous guidelines and other literature produced by local government offices and national heritage organisations, which provide standards and advice on archaeology and heritage matters in general. However, their specialised and technical language can mean they are often inaccessible to key decision makers in the development sector.

This guide provides the development sector with a unified accessible source of independent and practical advice and information regarding archaeology, drawing on the array of existing guidance. It is illustrated by a series of case studies showing good practice, and a few cautionary examples of less well-planned events that have led to difficulties both for developers and the archaeological heritage.

This good practice guidance has been written for clients, designers and investors, and for all members of the professional teams, including archaeologists, involved with development and construction dealing with sites of known or potential archaeological interest.

Archaeology and development

Acknowledgements

Research contractor

This guidance is the outcome of CIRIA Research Project 741. It was prepared by the Museum of London Archaeology Service (MoLAS) with the assistance of the Institute of Field Archaeologists (IFA) and Scott Wilson Ltd.

Authors

Bruno Barber is a senior archaeologist with MoLAS, with particular experience in field archaeology, implementing mitigation schemes, and post-excavation research, authorship and management.

Jay Carver is an associate with Scott Wilson Ltd. He has advised on numerous development projects, including the Channel Tunnel Rail Link and Crossrail projects. He has authored good practice guidance for the Highways Agency.

Peter Hinton is the chief executive of the Institute of Field Archaeologists (IFA), the professional body for archaeologists in the UK. He has worked in archaeology since 1973, including a period as head of Specialist Services at MoLAS.

Taryn Nixon is the managing director of the Museum of London Archaeology Service. With a background in project management and consultancy, she has worked in commercial archaeology since 1987. She is a former chair of the IFA and a member of the CABE Design Review specialist panel.

Contributors

Contributions were provided by Kenneth Aitchison (IFA), Simon McCudden and Andy Mayes (Scott Wilson Ltd). The project manager for the Research Contractor was Peter Rowsome (MoLAS).

Following CIRIA's usual practice the research was guided by a Steering Group, with the following members:

Steve Ball	English Partnerships
Gareth Brown (chair)	Bovis Lend Lease (Project Slam)
Patrick Browne	Skanska
Noel Fojut	Historic Scotland
Kirsty Jones	Thames Water
Ed Lee	English Heritage
Jenny MacDonnell	British Council for Offices
Trevor Mitchell	Land Securities
Taryn Nixon (chair)	Museum of London Archaeology Service
Ray Robinson	Aon Ltd

CIRIA C672

London, 2008

Archaeology and development

– a good practice guide to managing risk and maximising benefit

Bruno Barber   Museum of London Archaeology Service

Jay Carver   Scott Wilson Ltd

Peter Hinton   Institute of Field Archaeologists

Taryn Nixon   Museum of London Archaeology Service

Books are to

CIRIA *sharing knowledge ▪ building best practice*

Classic House, 174–180 Old Street, London EC1V 9BP
TELEPHONE 020 7549 3300
FAX 020 7253 0523
EMAIL   enquiries@ciria.org
WEBSITE   www.ciria.org

Archaeology and development – a good practice guide to managing risk and maximising benefit

Barber, B, Carver, J, Hinton, P, Nixon, T

CIRIA

CIRIA C672   © CIRIA 2008   RP741   ISBN: 978-0-86017-672-5

British Library Cataloguing in Publication Data

A catalogue record for this book is available from the British Library

Keywords		
Contaminated land, environmental good practice, ground engineering, piling		
Reader interest	**Classification**	
Archaeology, environment, contaminated land, land development, construction	AVAILABILITY	Open publication
	CONTENT	Advice/guidance
	STATUS	Committee-guided
	USER	Land owners, developers, planning officers, environmental and engineering consultants, investors

Published by CIRIA, Classic House, 174-180 Old Street, London EC1V 9BP, UK

Peter Rowsome	Museum of London Archaeology Service
Mike de Silva	Transport for London/Davis Langdon LLP
Ken Smith	Peak District National Park
Paul Wheelhouse (chair)	Golder Associates
Robert Whytehead	English Heritage
Alex Woodcraft	CIRIA

CIRIA's research managers for the project were Sarah Reid and Alex Woodcraft.

Project funders

This project was funded by: British Council for Offices, Crown Estates, English Partnerships, English Heritage, Historic Scotland, Land Securities, Thames Water, Transport for London, CIRIA Core Programme.

Source materials

Thanks to the following individuals and organisations for providing case study material, illustrations, additional external advice etc:

Nick Bateman (MoLAS), British Land Plc, Patrick Browne (Skanska), English Heritage, Alan Gilbertson (CIRIA), Glamorgan Gwent Archaeological Trust, Highways Agency, Institute of Field Archaeologists, Trevor Mitchell (Land Securities), Mike Morris (Chester Archaeology Service), Museum of London Archaeology Service, Taryn Nixon (Museum of London Archaeology Service), Pre-Construct Archaeology Ltd, Caroline Rawle (Welwyn Hatfield Museums Service), Ray Robinson (Aon Ltd), Tony Rook, Paul Thomas (Galliford), Scott Wilson Ltd, Union Railways Ltd, Alex Woodcraft (CIRIA).

Front cover image courtesy MoLAS.

Contents

List of case studies

Archaeology and development

List of figures

Glossary

Archaeology	The scientific study of past human cultures by analysing the material remains (sites and artefacts) that people left behind.
Archaeological remains	The term generally used to describe the material, including deposits such as soils and associated artefacts and ecofacts, found on archaeological sites. There is often an overlap with built heritage where archaeological sites and monuments contain architectural elements although sometimes the term is used to distinguish between buried soft deposits and built heritage that has architectural elements and/or upstanding, above-ground archaeology.
Archaeological feature	A generic term for a pit or a ditch, or anything that has historically dug into the ground.
Archaeological monitoring	Archaeological monitoring involves an archaeologist being present in the course of carrying out development works (which may include conservation works), to identify and protect archaeological deposits, features or objects that may be uncovered or otherwise affected by the works (see also *Watching brief*).
Archaeological risk	The potential for archaeological remains or other cultural heritage assets on, beneath or adjacent to a site to impose constraints, costs and/or delays on a development/construction programme. Like any other risk, it can be anticipated, managed and reduced.
Archive	The record of an individual archaeological investigation or series of investigations as part of a single project (field records, photographs, artefacts, environmental remains, written analysis, digital information, written report). Usually deposited for long-term curation with an appropriate local museum.
Artefact	An object or part of an object that has been used or created by a human and provides physical clues to the activity carried out by humans in the area of discovery. This can range from pottery, metalwork, woodwork, worked stones through to mortar samples (see also *Environmental remains*).
Assemblage	A group of artefacts found together in a single context such as a grave or pit.
Built heritage	An individual (or group thereof) building, structure, monument, installation or remains that is associated with architectural, cultural, social, political, economic, or military history. Forms part of the cultural or economic remains of human development. Sites with a built heritage component often also contain below-ground archaeological remains.
Client	The individual or organisation that has undertaken to fund the programme of archaeological works. Often the client is the developer or applicant seeking planning permission.

Consultant	An expert providing objective and independent advice to the developer on the basis of professional standards. Their work entails seeking the best solution for their client through negotiation with the planning archaeologist.
Conservation area	An area of special architectural or historic interest, the character or appearance of which it is desirable to preserve or enhance.
Conservation area consent	The permission needed to demolish or alter any building or other structure within a conservation area as designated in a local plan. Approvals are given by the local authority.
Consultation	The process required in the context of town planning wherein the prospective developer liaises with the relevant agencies (such as English Heritage, the Environment Agency, local government), community and special interest groups and the general public.
Context	A single unit of archaeological material or a feature, which is often referred to numerically, and can be any feature, layer or single element of a structure. A pit or ditch, for example, would have a context number for the cut and a separate number for each fill within the cut.
Contractor	A person or organisation usually commissioned by the client to undertake archaeological research and/or fieldwork according to a brief or general requirement for archaeological investigation set by a planning archaeologist (archaeological advisor).
County/city archaeologist	An archaeologist employed by a county council or city council who acts as the curator responsible for that local government area. The county/city archaeologist is responsible for archaeological matters within the county/city and will maintain the Sites and Monuments Record (also curatorial archaeologist, planning archaeologist and heritage/community archaeologist).
Cultural heritage/ cultural assets	The term often used in Environmental Statements to encompass the totality of archaeological sites, historic buildings and historic landscapes (as defined by the Department for Transport (DfT) and the Highways Agency). An individual archaeological site(s) or structure(s), a monument or group of monuments, an historic building(s), or historic landscape(s).

The general conference of UNESCO has defined cultural heritage as:

- **monuments:** architectural works, works of monumental sculpture and painting, including cave dwellings and inscriptions, and elements, groups of elements or structures of special value from the point of view of archaeology, history, art or science

- **groups of buildings:** groups of separate or connected buildings, which because of their architecture, their homogeneity or their place in the landscape, are of special value from the point of view of history, art or science

- **sites:** topographical areas, the combined works of man and of nature, which are of special value by reason of their beauty or their interest from the archaeological, historical, ethnological or anthropological point of view.

Recommendation concerning the national level protection of the cultural and natural heritage (UNESCO, 1972).

Desk-based assessment	"... a programme of assessment of the known or potential archaeological resource within a specified area or site ... It consists of a collation of existing written, graphic, photographic and electronic information in order to identify the likely character, extent, quality and worth of the known or potential archaeological resource in a local, regional, national or international context as appropriate." (IFA 2001a).
Development control	Under the various Planning Acts, the functions of the planning authority in deciding on planning applications and enforcing compliance with the planning laws.
Enforcement notice	The statutory notification of breach of condition or planning permission PPG 16, Section 172.
Environmental Impact Assessment	Often contracted to EIA is "a process which identifies the environmental effects (both negative and positive) of development proposals. It aims to prevent, reduce and offset any adverse impacts" (Scottish Executive, PAN58).
Environmental remains	May include any preserved organic material such as pollen, seeds, insects and any other animal remains (sometimes replaced by the term ecofact).
Environmental Statement	The report resulting from the first stage (data collection and assessment) of an EIA, which accompanies a planning application.
Excavation	A programme of controlled, intrusive fieldwork with defined research objectives that examines and records archaeological deposits, features and structures and, as appropriate, retrieves artefacts, environmental and other remains within a specified area or site (on land or underwater). The records made and objects gathered during fieldwork are studied and the results of that study published in detail appropriate to the project design and in the light of findings.
Field evaluation (trial trenching)	A limited programme of non-intrusive and/or intrusive fieldwork that determines the presence or absence of archaeological features, structures, deposits, artefacts or ecofacts within a specified area or site on land or underwater. If such archaeological remains are present field evaluation defines their character, extent and relative quality, as well as enabling assessment of their worth in a local, regional, national or international context as appropriate.
Field walking	A form of intrusive (has a physical impact) evaluation that aims to provide information on the presence of occupation and the periods represented on a site by the collection of surface artefacts. Usually takes placed on ploughed agricultural land.

Geophysical survey	A technical, non-intrusive (no impact) method of estimating what may be present beneath the ground surface. A number of methodologies are available, including ground penetrating radar (GPR), resistivity and magnetometry (see Gaffney and Gater, 2003). Specialist operation of the field equipment is required and interpretation of the data is sometimes difficult. However, geophysical survey can be very effective, though it is very dependent on soil and geological conditions within the site area.
Heritage	Properties and artefacts of cultural importance handed down from the past (as defined by the Department of Culture, Media and Sport).
Heritage asset	Any component of the historic environment.
Historic environment	The currently accepted UK term for the context in which heritage assets are managed. Section 6.1 of Planning Policy Guidance Note 15 defines the historic environment as "those aspects of the country that reflect the shaping hand of human history" (PPG15, 1994). Historic environment may come to be used in place of cultural heritage in Environmental Statements.
Historic Environment (HERs)	A record held by records planning authorities of all reported archaeological sites and finds, from the prehistoric to the post-medieval. The database is constantly kept up-to-date and is the starting point for most archaeological research, be it for educational or for planning purposes. HERs are the mainly local authority-based services used for planning, but they also operate a public service and play a role in education. These records were previously known as Sites and Monuments Records (SMRs), the name being changed to reflect the wider scope of the data they now contain.
Historic landscapes	These comprise type areas and zones within the historic environment that can be recognised at the macro (or landscape) scale. They maybe designated in some way, such as historic battlefields and historic parks and gardens, or undesignated zones that preserve important vernacular landscapes such as ancient field systems, woodland or indeed urban landscapes.
Historic parks and gardens	These range from town gardens and public parks to the great country estates. English Heritage owns a number of these but many are in private ownership. A number of the most important sites have been included on the English Heritage register of parks and gardens of special historic interest. Although the register has no statutory power, Planning Policy Guidance Note 15 indicates that the effect of proposed development on a registered park or garden or its setting is a material consideration in the determination of a planning application. It is important to protect such sites from new road schemes and new developments.
In situ	Refers to archaeological remains in their original place, usually in the context of a mitigation option that results in the preservation *in situ* of archaeological deposits.

Landscape archaeology	Placing sites into a wider context using a full range of archaeological, environmental and historical information to interpret them on a regional basis on a long-term scale (see also *Historic landscapes*).
Listed buildings	A listed building is one included in a statutory list of buildings of special architectural or historic interest compiled by the Secretary of State in England.
Listed building consent	The consent needed to do works to a listed building. This is applied for through the local authority and is only one of a number of permissions that may be required for any works.
Material Assets	A term used in Parts I and II of Schedule 4 to the Town and Country Planning (Environmental Impact Assessment) (England and Wales) Regulations 1999, referring to the architectural and archaeological heritage. Archaeological remains are sometimes handled under this heading in the planning process.
Mitigation	Action(s) taken to reduce the potential for damage to a heritage asset through avoiding development, design solutions, or recording in advance of damage.
National Monuments Record (NMR)	Parallel NMRs exist as part of English Heritage, Historic Scotland and the Royal Commission on the Ancient and Historical Monuments of Wales, providing historic environment and archaeological information services to the public, academics and commercial organisations based on a range of archive and information resources. In Scotland these are now known as the collections of the RCAHMS and in Northern Ireland the Monuments and Buildings Record.
Overburden	The material deposits between ground level and the underlying archaeological deposits. Note that made ground, as commonly described in engineering texts, borehole logs and so on, generally includes the man-made deposits that are the main focus of archaeological interest.
Planning Policy Guidance (PPG)	Documents produced by the British Government to advise local planning authorities on the planning process. PPG16: *Archaeology and planning* sets out the secretary of states policy on archaeological remains on land, and how they should be preserved or recorded.
Planning conditions	Conditions attached to a planning permission under the Planning Acts.
Planning statement	An additional report, usually to accompany applications for full planning permission, setting out details of what assessment and evaluation work has been conducted, the nature of the heritage assets, and the mitigation measures proposed should permission be granted.
Pre-determination	Archaeological investigations required to inform the planning archaeologist before an official decision on the scheme is given. This may include desk-based assessments, intrusive evaluation, geophysics, field survey and other methods of collecting enough information on the site to allow for an informed decision to be made.

Preservation by record	The phrase used in PPG16 to describe the mitigation option by which archaeological remains are said to be replaced or preserved for future study in the archive. Sometimes published in a report following an archaeological investigation.
Public archaeology	The presentation of archaeology to the public.
Redevelopment	New construction or conversion, usually by the private sector but often with public sector support or participation, of previously developed land and/or buildings
Risk	The probability that a (generally adverse) effect will occur under defined conditions (see also *Archaeological risk*).
Risk assessment	The process of assessing the hazards and risks associated with a particular site or group of sites.
Risk estimation	A conceptual stage of risk assessment, concerned with estimating the likelihood that an adverse effect will result from exposure of archaeological remains to the development.
Risk evaluation	A conceptual stage of risk assessment (generally following risk estimation) concerned with evaluating the acceptability of accepted risks, taking into account:

- the nature and scale of risk estimates

- any uncertainties associated with the assessment

- the broad costs and benefits of taking action to mitigate the risks.

Risk management	The process whereby decisions are made to accept a known or assessed risk and/or the implementation of action to reduce the consequences or probabilities of occurrence.
Sections	Vertical records of stratigraphy revealed by excavation and recorded in drawings and photographs as evidence of the sequence of contexts on a site.
Scheduled Monument (Scheduled Ancient Monument in Scotland)	Sites and monuments deemed to be of national importance, which are given legal protection by being placed on a list or schedule. English Heritage takes the lead in identifying sites in England that should be placed on the schedule by the Secretary of State for Culture, Media and Sport. A schedule has been kept since 1882 of monuments whose preservation is given priority over other land uses. The current legislation, the Ancient Monuments and Archaeological Areas Act 1979, supports this formal system.
Scheduled Monument consent	As defined by the Ancient Monuments and Archaeological Areas Act 1979, Scheduled Monument consent is required by law to control any work to a Scheduled Monument. It is a criminal offence not to obtain consent in advance of works.
Sites and Monuments Record (SMR)	A written database archive, often stored and disseminated in digital format, of all archaeological sites and find locations from a given area, usually a county. An SMR is usually maintained by the planning authority and adopted by formal resolution. Now increasingly known as an Historic Environment Record (HER).

Archaeology and development

Stakeholder	Any individual, group or organisation that may affect, be affected by or perceive itself to be affected by archaeological risk.
Statutory consultee	National public organisation/bodies that need to be consulted on planning applications, depending on the level of archaeological potential.
Site archive	Contains all the information gathered during fieldwork and must be quantified, ordered, indexed and consistent. It represents the original record of the project's results.
Test pits	Small single or more usually multiple excavations that aim to provide an indication of the underlying soil/deposit profiles. These may take place prior to full evaluation, or may be all that is required on the site.
Trial trenching	See *Field evaluation*.
Urban archaeological database	A written database archive often stored and disseminated in digital format, of all archaeological sites and find locations from a given urban area, usually a single town or city and maintained by the local planning authority. See also *Sites and Monuments Record* (SMR).
Walkover survey	Visual inspection (on foot) of a site or linear route to collect data regarding surface conditions, topography, past and present land use etc, usually conducted as part of desk-based assessment.
Watching brief	A formal programme of observation and investigation agreed with the authorities conducted during any operation carried out for non-archaeological reasons within a specified area or site on land or underwater, where there is a possibility that archaeological deposits may be disturbed or destroyed. The programme will result in the preparation of a report and ordered archive, which is also paid for by the developer.
Written scheme of investigation	Often referred to as a WSI, sometimes also called a method statement or project design. A written proposal for archaeological investigation of whatever form (evaluation, excavation, watching brief etc) that is submitted to the local planning authority as a statement of intent by an archaeological organisation employed by a developer.

Acronyms and abbreviations

ADS	Archaeology data service
ALGAO	Association of Local Government Archaeological Officers (UK)
APM	Association of Project Managers
APPEAR	(European Commission) Accessibility Projects Sustainable Preservation and Enhancement of Urban Subsoil Archaeological Remains
BMAPA	British Marine Aggregate Producers Association
CBA	Council for British Archaeology
CDM	Construction (Design and Management) Regulations 2007
CIRIA	Construction Industry Research and Information Association
CTRL	Channel Tunnel Rail Link
DBA	Desk-based assessment
DCA	Department for Constitutional Affairs
DCLG	Department for Local Government
DCMS	Department for Culture Media and Sport
DEFRA	Department for Environment Food and Rural Affairs
DfT	Department for Transport
DMRB	(Highways Agency) Design Manual for Roads and Bridges
ECI	Early contractor involvement (Highways Agency contract)
ECC	Engineering and construction contract (Highways Agency contract)
EDD	Environmental due diligence
EH	English Heritage
EHTF	English Historic Towns Forum
EIA	Environmental Impact Assessment
ES	Environmental Statement
EU	European Union
GLAAS	English Heritage) Greater London Archaeological Advisory Service
GPS	Global positioning system
HELM	Historic environment local management project
HER	Historic Environment Record
HPA	Heritage Partnership Agreement
HSE	Health and Safety Executive
IAI	Institute of Archaeologists of Ireland
ICE	Institution of Civil Engineers
ICOMOS	International Council on Monuments and Sites
IFA	Institute of Field Archaeologists
ISA	Initial site appraisal
JCT	Joint contracts tribunal (form of contract)

JNAPC	Joint Nautical Archaeology Policy Committee
LB	London Borough
LPA	Local planning authority
MAP2	Management of archaeological projects 2 (English Heritage 1991)
MCA	Maritime and Coastguard Agency
MIP	Major infrastructure project
MoLAS	Museum of London Archaeology Service
NEC	New engineering contract (form of contract)
NMR	National Monuments Record
NMRS	National Monuments Record of Scotland
NPPG	National Planning Policy Guidance (Scotland)
OASIS	Online Access to the Index of Archaeological Investigations
OECD	Organisation for Economic Co-operation and Development
PAN	Planning Advice Note (Scotland)
PFI	Private finance initiative (funding mechanism and contract form)
PG	Planning Guidance (Wales)
PPG	Planning Policy Guidance (England)
PPP	Public Private Partnership (funding mechanism and contract form)
PPS	Planning Policy Statement (Northern Ireland and England)
RCAHMS	Royal Commission on the Ancient and Historical Monuments of Scotland
RCAHMW	Royal Commission on the Ancient and Historical Monuments of Wales
RAO	Registered archaeological organisation (IFA)
RIAS	Royal Institute of Architects in Scotland
RIBA	Royal Institute of British Architects
RICS	Royal Institution of Chartered Surveyors
RTPI	Royal Town Planning Institute
SMR	Sites and Monuments Record
SPG	Supplementary Planning Guidance
TAN	Technical Advice Note (Wales)
UAD	Urban archaeological database
UK	United Kingdom (England, Scotland, Wales and Northern Ireland)
UNESCO	United Nations Educational Scientific and Cultural Organisation
UPD	Updated project design
VCC	Vibro concrete column
WSI	Written scheme of investigation

1   Introduction

1.1   WHY IS ARCHAEOLOGY IMPORTANT TO THE DEVELOPMENT SECTOR?

In the UK the majority of archaeological endeavour takes place as a result of development. The most recent figures for England (1999/2000) indicate that central government and EU funds contributed £19m, local government £25m and developers £68m (Aitchison, 2002). Estimates for 2003/4 suggest similar figures for central and local government, and an increase to c£150m in developer spending.

Today archaeology is a significant element of construction and development, and all parties – developers, archaeologists and the regulatory authorities – should aim to ensure that good practice is applied and value for money is obtained.

Among the many reasons why the development sector should address archaeology are:

- **planning law, heritage law and planning policy:** archaeological remains are an important part of our shared cultural heritage, and they are a fragile, finite and irreplaceable resource that needs to be safeguarded. This is recognised within the UK planning process and by UK national legislation and guidance, European legislation, and guidance from international non-governmental organisations

   While some archaeological sites and remains are protected by statute, all archaeological remains affected by developments under planning are treated as material considerations in the planning process. Ignoring or misunderstanding the regulations and processes could result in refusal of an application, enforcement action, additional costs and delays.

   UK legislation and guidance have adopted the polluter pays principle (a feature of OECD and EU environmental directives), where the prospective developer manages the cost of assessing and mitigating development impacts on archaeological remains

- **education and new knowledge:** archaeology makes a significant contribution to education, social cohesion and the economy. Though sometimes perceived as a special interest academic subject, it brings wide public benefits and knowledge gained through archaeological work taught in schools and universities

- **economy and society:** archaeology underpins the UK's tourism and heritage industries, often directly creating jobs. It also plays an important indirect role in regeneration – a role increasingly recognised by developers – by invoking a sense of place and cultural identity for new developments

- **sustainability:** developers can demonstrate their commitment to sustainability and responsible development through a positive approach to archaeology, and also a recognition that archaeological remains are a precious and non-renewable resource requiring environmental protection and controls.

Archaeology and development

According to the Institution of Civil Engineers' rules of professional conduct:

"All members shall have full regard for the public interest, particularly in relation to matters of health and safety, and in relation to the well-being of future generations."

The guidance notes on the interpretation and application of the rules of professional conduct state that:

"Members should take account of the broader public interest – the interests of all stakeholders in any project must be taken properly into account, including the impact on future generations. This must include regard for the impact upon the society and quality of life of affected individuals, groups or communities, and upon their cultural, archaeological and ethnic heritage, and the broader interests of humanity as a whole"

(source: ICE, 2006)

◆ **effective risk management:** there is a widespread assumption within the industry that developments are often delayed by archaeology. While this is rare if handled incorrectly archaeology can have major adverse effects on development and construction, leading to unanticipated costs, design changes, programming delays and even litigation

◆ **well handled, archaeological remains can bring benefits to a development:** an early, positive and proactive approach to archaeological remains can help to provide historical or cultural depth to a scheme. It can offer a design context for a new scheme, and result in an increased sense of place for stakeholders/occupiers. Furthermore, archaeology can provide opportunities for community involvement and generate beneficial public relations credits for promoters even with controversial development schemes.

While archaeological remains can be a risk in development, it can be easily managed and controlled. The key principle for managing archaeological risk is illustrated in Figure 1.1. The further into a development project life cycle, the higher the cost of responding to unexpected archaeological discoveries.

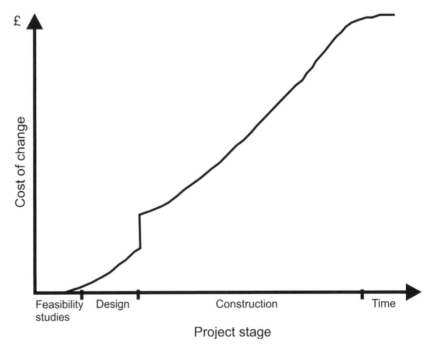

Figure 1.1 *Cost of change against project stage (after ICE, 1996)*

Background

Every developer's and construction professional's worst archaeological nightmare is the unexpected discovery of a nationally important monument on their site during construction, and for their programme to be disrupted by public protest, government intervention and the redesign of their scheme.

The case of the Rose Theatre, London in the late 1980s arose because of poor risk assessment in advance of development by both developers and archaeologists in the context of a weak planning regime. (Note this was before current policy on archaeology and development was introduced as PPG16). Because the exact location of the theatre was not known and its remains (which were assumed to have been destroyed) were only discovered at a critical point in the project process, archaeologists and developers initially found themselves in conflict, against the background of a high profile public campaign to save the remains, led by politicians and internationally known actors (Figure 1.2).

Figure 1.2

Dame Peggy Ashcroft and Dustin Hoffman were among the high-profile protesters at the Rose Theatre (courtesy MoLAS or Andy Fulgoni)

Outcome

The situation was eventually resolved but only after government intervention. A nationally important archaeological site was preserved for future generations (and monitoring points put in place to allow scientific study of the continuing ground conditions beneath the new building). However, this involved an extensive redesign of the new building's foundations, to bridge over the Rose Theatre remains, with massive delays and costs to the developer.

Lessons learned

◆ the organisation and management of the archaeological profession has changed as a result of this and similar cases. Indeed, this case served in some ways as a catalyst for introducing the new planning policy guidance note on archaeology (PPG16). Now, archaeologists, developers and their contractors are accustomed to working together in the context of a reformed planning system that adopts a risk-based approach. Such conflicts are far less likely to arise now as archaeological risks should be identified and defined at an early stage of the development and planning cycle, and later managed and controlled

◆ the advice in this guide should help to avoid similar situations arising in the future by emphasising careful risk assessment and management (Section 3.1). The case also highlights that until detailed site investigation takes place, unexpected discoveries cannot be ruled out and should be included in project planning.

(source: MoLAS)

Archaeology and development

Obtaining early specialist advice is vital for the developer. Consulting an archaeologist early on – even before a site is acquired – is beneficial because:

◆ significant archaeological remains – particularly if buried, or located in the intertidal zone or underwater – may only become apparent following specialist investigations. A developer requires as much information as possible to avoid surprises during the construction programme

◆ unlike a mineral resource, which may be extracted and used elsewhere, the value of the archaeological resource depends on its research potential. Specialist advice is needed to record and analyse the relationships between different layers, features, artefacts and environmental remains on the site and to provide a durable record for the national archive and for academic use by future generations. A developer will need to reassure planning authorities that appropriate expertise has been procured.

1.2   SCOPE OF THE GUIDANCE

This guidance is concerned primarily with the types of archaeological remains that are often not easily discernible and that require specialist skills to identify, assess and evaluate. This includes remains that are largely buried out of view of current land surfaces, or those that, although occupying the surface of the land, are not immediately apparent (for example subtle earthwork variations). The archaeology of historic buildings requires separate guidance. Information on handling historic buildings and the risks and opportunities surrounding their alteration, demolition, or re-use and the often associated issues of development within conservation areas is outside the scope of this guide. However indicators are provided where appropriate to useful resources on these subject matters.

This guidance addresses the main forms of archaeological risk likely to be encountered on development and construction projects in the UK (England, Wales, Scotland and Northern Ireland). Its focus is on the risks associated with the buried archaeological heritage, although some mention is made of above ground monuments, standing buildings and coastal/marine archaeology (Section 2.5.2), and portable objects (Section 2.5.4), together with references to more detailed sources of information (see *Bibliography* and *Further reading*).

Important legislation or guidelines that apply to all development and construction projects, and are not specific to those with an archaeological component are not addressed here other than specific health and safety considerations in Section 4.6.6.

1.3   AIMS AND OBJECTIVES

This guidance is intended primarily for the development sector. It aims to:

◆ provide independent and practical guidance on the consideration of archaeological remains on all types of development sites

◆ help the reader through the process of dealing with archaeology on any UK site

◆ show how common problems can be avoided and how programme delays and costs can be effectively controlled

◆ show how archaeological risk can be managed and to identify, manage and reduce (mitigate) potential adverse risks associated with poor practice or non-compliance during the planning, design and construction process (for example programme delays, risk to reputation, risk to investment)

- help readers gain a sound understanding of the key planning and legal requirements and when they arise

- ensure that developments run smoothly with the necessary consents and approvals in place

- demonstrate how archaeology may add value to or enhance development and produce positive outcomes

- provide checklists for development teams to enhance their ability to manage archaeology during the planning, design and construction stages of projects.

The good practice principles presented in this guide are based on the authors' and the steering group members' experience of a wide range of development projects across the UK where archaeological or built heritage issues have been encountered.

1.4   TARGET READERSHIP FOR THE GUIDE

This guidance has been written for a wide readership and is designed to be accessible to a range of professionals with limited experience of archaeological issues. The guide is aimed both at decision makers at the very early stages of a project's inception (for example project feasibility and land assembly stages) through to those responsible for designing, planning and undertaking development projects.

The guide is principally aimed at:

- **client organisations and promoters:** decision makers responsible for initiating and directing projects

- **development teams:** project managers, architects, engineers, town planners, quantity surveyors, archaeologists and other specialist consultants

- **construction teams:** contractors, construction planners and specialist sub-contractors.

The guide will also be a useful reference for:

- investors – those responsible for investing funds in a particular scheme

- insurance brokers and underwriters

- public sector decision makers.

1.5   BACKGROUND

In the UK there is increasing pressure to develop land. When a new development proposal is formed, it should be assumed until proven otherwise that even if land has been built upon before, archaeological remains may still survive. So the developer needs to provide sufficient information on the heritage of a site to enable the relevant planning and regulatory authorities to determine a planning proposal.

This requires the careful evaluation and treatment of archaeological remains as a business risk. Most archaeological remains can be successfully avoided or managed, and the affect of development on the remains (or vice versa) successfully mitigated through effective risk assessment.

If such remains are present, the developer's crucial first step will be to identify their exact nature and extent, and establish how they might affect a proposed development and the most effective way to manage them.

This requires a staged approach using the most appropriate desk-based assessment and field evaluation techniques, designed to obtain vital information about surviving remains. This information should be provided to the relevant authorities by the developer in support of the development proposal, for authorities to base planning decisions. Figure 1.3 illustrates the typical process of archaeology and development within the planning process.

UK planning policy now clearly sets out this staged approach (see Section 2.3 and Chapter 3) and archaeologists and developers have recognised the need to consider archaeological remains within a risk management framework and the value of addressing archaeology early.

In the 1970s and 80s poor communication or a lack of understanding may have created an impasse between the conservation and development sectors. Today archaeologists, developers and other design and construction professionals appreciate and share each others' objectives because preserving heritage is seen as important. Increasing archaeological professionalism has seen archaeologists included in development design teams. The responsibility for protecting heritage lies with local and national authorities, so commercial archaeologists now work with and on behalf of developers. This guide illustrates many examples where archaeology has been avoided, or remains protected and development impact minimised through design solutions (Section 4.4).

As each archaeological site and each development is different, there is continuing demand for accurate and accessible information on effectively managing archaeology during construction, and pragmatic lessons and good practice guidance based on direct experience.

1.6 DEFINITIONS

A detailed glossary is provided on page xii. The term *historic environment* is preferred both in government policies and the planning system when referring to archaeological remains. This includes historic built heritage and historic landscapes and townscapes that provide the context and character for much of the UK's archaeological and architectural history. Further sub-divisions can be made to distinguish archaeological remains from built heritage and historic landscapes. Section 7.1 of the planning policy guidance note 15 defines the historic environment as "those aspects of the country that reflect the shaping hand of human history" (PPG15, 1994).

Cultural heritage is also commonly used in planning and Environmental Statements. However, it now has extended meanings associated with cultural property, including material assets and those of an intellectual nature such as wider arts and community values.

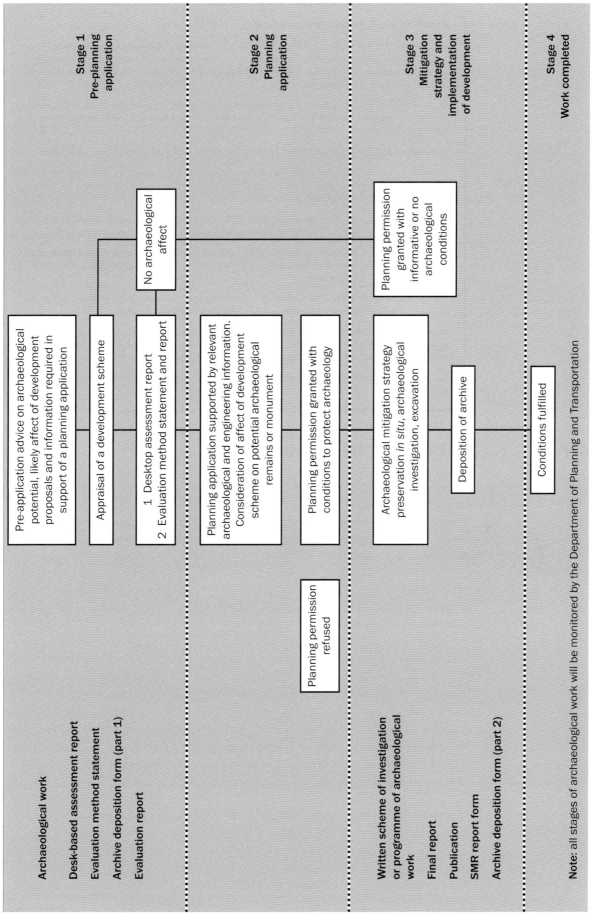

Figure 1.3   *Flow chart showing the archaeological process within a typical development project (from ICE, 2004b)*

Stage 1
Pre-planning
application

Stage 2
Planning
application

Stage 3
Mitigation
strategy and
implementation
of development

Stage 4
Work completed

Pre-application advice on archaeological potential, likely affect of development proposals and information required in support of a planning application

Appraisal of a development scheme

1 Desktop assessment report
2 Evaluation method statement and report

No archaeological affect

Planning application supported by relevant archaeological and engineering information. Consideration of affect of development scheme on potential archaeological remains or monument

Planning permission granted with conditions to protect archaeology

Planning permission refused

Planning permission granted with informative or no archaeological conditions

Archaeological mitigation strategy preservation *in situ*, archaeological investigation, excavation

Deposition of archive

Conditions fulfilled

Archaeological work

Desk-based assessment report

Evaluation method statement

Archive deposition form (part 1)

Evaluation report

Written scheme of investigation or programme of archaeological work

Final report

Publication

SMR report form

Archive deposition form (part 2)

Note: all stages of archaeological work will be monitored by the Department of Planning and Transportation

7

Archaeology and development

Recorded and legally protected assets

Most archaeological sites and finds are not legally protected. Many are listed in regional and private Historic Environment Records (HERs), or in Sites and Monuments Records (SMRs) and urban archaeological databases. Others are awaiting entry into these records and an unknown number remain to be discovered.

As an indication of the extent of known non-designated assets 18 000 (pre 18th century) sites and monuments are recorded in Northern Ireland and more than 1.43m in England (English Heritage, 2007a)

The designated (and so legally protected) heritage assets in the UK in 2007 were as follows:

England	372 769 listed building entries, 19 711 Scheduled Monuments, 9374 conservation areas, 1590 registered parks and gardens, 43 historic battlefields.
Scotland	47 329 listed buildings, 7782 Scheduled Monuments, 628 conservation areas, 386 registered parks and gardens (designed landscapes).
Wales	29 866 listed building entries, 3909 Scheduled Monuments, 511 conservation areas, 359 registered parks and gardens, 58 historic landscapes.
Northern Ireland	9000 listed building entries (approx), 1704 Scheduled Monuments, 59 conservation areas, 152 registered parks and gardens.

In the UK there are 58 designated wreck sites under the Protection of Wrecks Act 1973. The UK now has 27 World Heritage Sites of which 17 are in England, four in Scotland, two in Wales, one in Northern Ireland and three in overseas territories (English Heritage, 2007a).

See Section 2.5.2 for information on the legal status and handling of change to protected sites and buildings.

1.7 STRUCTURE OF THIS GUIDANCE

This guidance is designed for the use of professionals who seek to understand and manage archaeological risk in the context of development and construction. It can be read in its entirety by those with little or no experience of dealing with archaeological issues. It is also designed to be dipped into by anyone seeking advice on a particular issue or project stage.

The advice is aligned where appropriate with standard project stages common to many UK development processes such as the RIBA guidelines (RIBA, 2007) and the *Design manual for roads and bridges* (HA, 1992–2007).

The document is presented as follows:

Chapter 1 describes the scope, purpose and structure of this guidance.

Chapter 2 provides the background and framework for how archaeology and the wider historic environment is regulated and managed in the UK. How and when developers can take advice and contract services to ensure successful management of archaeological risks and opportunities.

Chapter 3 deals with archaeological risk and the keys to successful archaeological risk management.

Chapter 4 describes the typical processes in the life cycle of a project, illustrated where appropriate with flow charts and case studies. There is a strong emphasis on the processes of early risk assessment and later risk management.

Chapter 5 offers practical advice on achieving good practice. The processes described in Chapter 3 are illustrated with a series of case studies in Section 5.3. There are examples of how archaeology can be beneficial for developers, the public and educational facilities.

Appendix A1 contains a list of contact details for the government departments and national bodies responsible for archaeology in the UK.

A **glossary** and list of **acronyms** used in this text follows the contents.

A **bibliography** followed by **further reading** and **useful websites** is included.

Key guidance sections are provided throughout the guide to highlight the main points and provide direction to more detailed sources where relevant.

Key guidance: archaeology and development

Archaeological remains are part of our collective heritage. They have an inherent value for education, research, leisure, tourism and the economy. However they are a finite, non-renewable resource and so the potentially damaging affects of development requires mitigation.

An early, positive and proactive approach to archaeological remains can:

◆ minimise impacts (with benefits to developers in the form of increased cost certainty and more effective risk management)

◆ provide a research dividend that is acceptable mitigation in response to approved destruction of the resource

◆ help to provide historical or cultural context for new development

◆ ensure an increased sense of place for new communities

◆ provide opportunities for community involvement and generate beneficial publicity even for controversial development schemes.

Some archaeological sites and remains are protected by statute but all archaeological remains are treated by planning authorities as a material consideration in the planning process. Ignoring or postponing the assessment and evaluation of archaeological risk for a particular scheme can result in costly delay or even litigation. Early consideration of archaeology can present opportunities to use heritage assets to add value to a scheme.

It is crucial to address archaeological issues as early as possible. The potential for significant remains – particularly if buried, or located in the intertidal zone or underwater – may only be apparent following specialist investigations.

---

2 Archaeology in the UK: a summary

2.1 WHERE ARCHAEOLOGICAL REMAINS ARE FOUND

Archaeological remains – the physical evidence for past human activity and human interaction with the environment – can be encountered on most types of development site:

♦ **greenfield:** these are sites that are not developed at present, but which may have been in the past and contain remains of past settlement or land-use (for example a Bronze Age field system or a medieval village). Historic parks, gardens and other designed historic landscapes are also of archaeological significance

♦ **brownfield:** these are sites of previously developed land, whether in built-up or rural settings commonly used for industrial or commercial purposes. Here, permanent structures may be of archaeological significance and in town centres a long history of human occupation may have left a sequence of complex buried deposits.

The cost of archaeological assessment for brownfield redevelopment sites tends to be higher. Planning guidance across the UK has increased the pressure to develop brownfield sites. Notably, remediation of contaminated land can often conflict with archaeological mitigation (Environment Agency, 2005), so early co-ordination is essential (see CIRIA, 2002 and HSE, 1991).

Figure 2.1   *A 19th century pottery kiln found on a brownfield site (courtesy MoLAS)*

- **bluefield:** these are brownfield sites with a considerable water frontage. They are a significant site class for archaeology due to the increased risk of deeply stratified alluvial soils, and with high potential for good preservation of buried archaeological remains and palaeo-environmental remains. Bluefield sites can also contain evidence of past river management regimes and submerged landscapes, and require specialised methods of site assessment and evaluation

- **marine:** these are sites that have archaeological remains on the foreshore and seabed including shipwrecks, structures and submerged landscapes etc. Marine sites may also be categorised as bluefield sites.

Archaeological remains may occur in urban, suburban or rural contexts, on inland, coastal or floodplain land, on the foreshore or on the seabed and on single development schemes or linear projects.

2.2 TYPES OF ARCHAEOLOGICAL REMAINS

Archaeological remains can range from the mundane to the spectacular, although their importance may not be immediately apparent to the non-professional. Assessment of importance or significance can be subjective and opinions may differ between professionals and even between adjacent local authorities. Recent reforms to Scheduled Monument designation in Scotland, and proposed reforms to a wide range of historic assets in England and Wales (DCMS/WAG, 2007), are making the criteria for affording legal protection to archaeological remains more transparent and explicit. However, it will be some time before this discipline is consistently applied to the majority of archaeological sites. Some 98 per cent of archaeological sites lack legal protection but because they are considered as material to a planning application they present a risk to development.

Figure 2.2 contains a range of common examples that illustrate the types of remains often encountered, alongside the key issues they raise for developers.

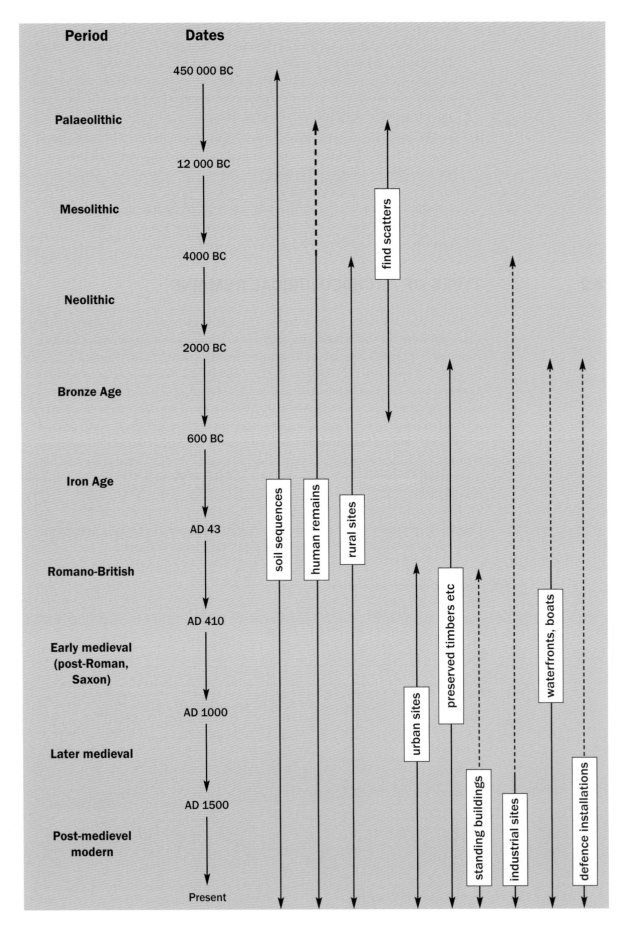

Period	Dates									
	450 000 BC									
Palaeolithic										
	12 000 BC										
Mesolithic				find scatters						
	4000 BC									
Neolithic										
	2000 BC									
Bronze Age										
	600 BC									
Iron Age		soil sequences	human remains	rural sites						
	AD 43									
Romano-British						preserved timbers etc				
	AD 410								waterfronts, boats	
Early medieval (post-Roman, Saxon)										
	AD 1000				urban sites					
Later medieval							standing buildings			
	AD 1500							industrial sites		
Post-medievel modern										defence installations
	Present									

Figure 2.2   *Time line showing chronological periods and the broad range of archaeological sites/ remains associated with them (courtesy MoLAS)*

- **find scatters:** important evidence for early human activity may survive only as scatters of flint tools and animal bone, as at the Palaeolithic site in Boxgrove, West Sussex. Hard to identify except in careful hand excavation or through chance finds (eg during gravel extraction). Time consuming to excavate and record

- **preserved timbers and organic material:** unusual burial conditions, particularly on waterlogged sites, may lead to the preservation of fragile plant remains or timber structures such as the Bronze Age trackways of the Somerset levels or Essex marshes. May have implications for any proposed de-watering and piling operations. Preserved timbers may also be found in urban contexts where, for example, waterfronts, timber drains, or well-linings lie beneath the water table. Excellent preservation (eg of wood, leather and textile that do not survive elsewhere) can result in substantial off-site (environmental processing, analysis and finds/timber conservation work) costs. Riverside or coastal sites may contain evidence of former waterfront structures, ranging from simple riverbank revetments to complex harbour installations, as well as associated waterlogged deposits and remains

- **sediment/soil sequences** buried beneath a site may contain evidence (pollen, waterlogged plant remains, snail shells etc) that can be used to understand the environmental context in which people lived. May be deeply buried. Not obvious to non-specialists.

Figure 2.3   *Geoarchaeological work in progress on deep sedimentary sequence (courtesy MoLAS)*

- **rural sites:** for example, pits and ditches in villages and farmsteads can reveal the layout of fields and enclosures, their use for arable and pasture, and the dates and character of the settlements they sustained. They are often characterised by shallow archaeological deposits. They are easily damaged by construction activities, though relatively straightforward to excavate.

Archaeology and development

Figure 2.4   *Pits and ditches under excavation on a rural site (courtesy MoLAS)*

◆ **urban sites:** historic city and town centres are usually characterised by deeper, more complex archaeological sequences, in some cases many metres deep. Remains on urban sites are often logistically more challenging to investigate – they may be deeper, require shoring, be less accessible or waterlogged etc. Archaeological costs on urban sites, as well as the attendant enabling works costs, tend to be higher. As deposits are often finds-rich, the post-excavation analysis and publication costs can also be higher

◆ **burial remains/cemetery:** human remains are a rich source of archaeological information, and they may be encountered unexpectedly or as part of the deliberate clearance of a disused burial ground. These sites may be subject to specific statutory and religious legislation and require separate permissions. Off-site (post-excavation analysis and publication) costs may be high

◆ **standing and buried archaeology:** some sites contain both buried archaeological deposits as well as standing structures for example the medieval Torre Abbey, Torquay (Devon). Site investigation and archaeological recording of buried and built archaeology should be designed and implemented in a unified manner so that the work leads to a coherent record.

Figure 2.5
Windsor Castle: standing and buried archaeology (courtesy MoLAS)

- **boats and wrecks:** these sites are found in rivers, coastal and marine areas. It is important to understand that in many areas river regimes, sea levels and coastlines have been subject to change over archaeological timescales. Similar problems as for preserved timbers and waterfronts. Nationally important finds may be costly if lifting and/or conservation is required (eg Case study 5.12)

- **former land surfaces and associated evidence for human activity:** these remains may now be underwater or sealed beneath alluvium due to changes in sea level or coastal morphology. Sites are often deeply buried and can be difficult and technically challenging to access and survey

- **industrial remains:** structures or features on brownfield sites, whether above- or below-ground, may be considered as cultural heritage assets, for example a well-preserved 19th century gasworks (Figure 2.6) or a 20th century industrial site with a documented origin during the Industrial Revolution (Figure 2.1).

Figure 2.6
A gasworks: potentially important industrial archaeology (courtesy MoLAS)

- **defence installations:** structures such as a Second World War airfield and associated structures, a Cold War civil defence headquarters or Napoleonic coastal defences may also be considered as cultural heritage assets and require survey, recording and protection.

2.3 ARCHAEOLOGICAL TECHNIQUES AND MITIGATION OPTIONS

If archaeological remains are present on or beneath a site a variety of techniques may be employed to assess, investigate or protect them. Archaeological remains are finite and fragile so planning authorities tend to categorise these techniques as:

- **non-intrusive:** not affecting the remains directly or indirectly

- **intrusive:** affecting and by implication potentially damaging or destroying archaeological remains.

Planning authorities are more likely to use non-intrusive techniques as far as possible during desk-based assessment and evaluation, so that if a decision is taken to protect important remains *in situ*, they will not have been adversely affected or altered.

2.3.1   Non-intrusive

Non-intrusive surveys are generally the first step in considering a prospective development. They form part of the established process by which developers, archaeologists and regulatory authorities will begin to identify the nature and extent of archaeological remains on a given development. Specifically, these surveys include:

- **desk-based assessment:** a desk-based assessment collates existing written, graphic, photographic and electronic information relating to a specified area or site (whether on land, in the intertidal zone or underwater), for the developer to present to the relevant planning or regulatory authority. It will involve a search of the local Historic Environment Record (HER) and work should also include a site visit or walkover survey. The purpose of the assessment is to identify the likely character, extent, quality and worth of the known and potential archaeological resource in a local, regional, national or international context. A developer should expect the study to conform to the IFA standard and guidance for desk-based assessments (IFA, 2001a). The report should include an assessment of the likely impacts of proposed development on archaeological remains, and consideration of mitigation options that may remove or reduce those impacts. If existing data are insufficient, the study may propose further non-intrusive or intrusive surveys. It is important for the development team to note that the desk-based assessment report is produced in support of their planning application. It is not necessarily a risk assessment for them but rather a report for them to submit for the planning authority to consider.

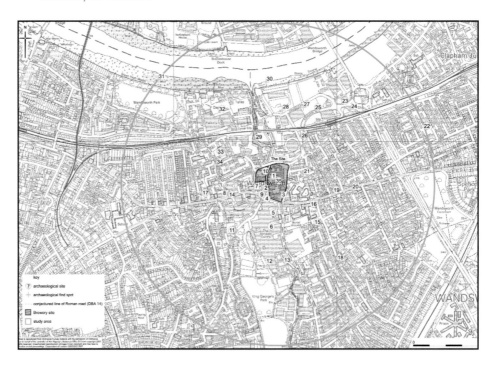

Figure 2.7   *A simple search of the relevant Sites and Monuments Record (SMR) or Historic Environment Record (HER) may indicate potential archaeological risk on site (courtesy MoLAS)*

- **aerial photography:** often carried out as part of a desk-based assessment, aerial photography can reveal archaeological features that may not be apparent from the ground. It has particular use in open and rural settings, but can also reveal changes in land-use and the built heritage in an urban context. Collections of military and civilian aerial photographs are held by the National Monuments Records (NMR) for England, Scotland and Wales and by some local authority archaeology officers

♦ **topographic survey:** a simple site survey is often required to record archaeological features such as banks, ditches and waterfront revetments. Topographic surveys may be required as part of desk-based assessments and base-line studies for Environmental Impact Assessments.

Figure 2.8
Surveying archaeological features in the intertidal zone (courtesy MoLAS)

♦ **remote sensing:** various techniques are available that allow the rapid recording and enhancement of features across a landscape, including those not easily identified in visible light. Among these is LIDAR (airborne light detection and ranging), which uses a pulsed laser beam to measure the height of the ground surface and other features with high resolution and accuracy

♦ **geophysical survey:** remote sensing techniques are often used to identify and interpret buried archaeological features. Techniques include ground penetrating radar (GPR), magnetic susceptibility, and magnetometer survey and resistivity survey. Each technique is suited to different soil types and ground conditions, and the nature of modern overburden and specialist advice is essential (see English Heritage, 1995 and Gaffney and Gater, 2003)

♦ **underwater survey:** techniques such as sonar and magnetometry can be carried out remotely from a boat to locate archaeological remains such as shipwrecks and structures, as well as features or surfaces buried in silt and metal objects on the seabed. Diving may also be carried out non-intrusively, and may involve photography, photogrammetry and measured drawings

♦ **standing building survey:** although outside the scope of this guide, it is appropriate to note that initial archaeological survey may identify important buildings or structural elements that require further assessment and/or consideration in the context of a particular development proposal.

2.3.2   Intrusive

Any works that involve disturbing below-ground archaeological deposits or structures are considered intrusive. Nonetheless it may be necessary to disturb archaeological remains to provide the developer and the planning authority with information to determine the nature, extent and significance of the remains, and to decide how best those remains should be treated.

All intrusive archaeological investigations will require detailed documentation in a project design and, no matter how small the works, will produce a project archive requiring deposition in an appropriate archive repository:

- **field walking:** a walkover survey that involves collection of surface artefacts, for example on ploughed fields and foreshore areas, is considered intrusive. Field walking can be an important tool in the identification of past human activity, and buried and/or otherwise invisible archaeological features

- **trial trenching:** trial trenches and test pits are commonly excavated to evaluate the nature, precise extent and potential (including the significance) of archaeological remains and may test the assumptions made during preceding desk-based assessment. Trial trenching is perhaps the most common technique in field evaluation, the aim of which is defined by the IFA as: "to gain information about the archaeological resource within a given area or site (including its presence or absence, character, extent, date, integrity, state of preservation and quality)" (IFA, 2001c)

- **geoarchaeological survey:** in some cases a more rigorous approach to evaluating buried archaeological deposits is appropriate. On some sites and linear projects, particularly in areas where surface topography bears little relationship to old land surfaces (for example when obscured by alluvial or colluvial deposits) these techniques can be used to model natural topography and the sequence of overlying historic deposits. This type of survey uses data to identify likely areas of archaeological interest

- **watching brief on engineering and construction works:** observation by archaeologists of works is sometimes specified as part of field evaluation for example observation of geotechnical test pits and boreholes can be cost-effective and, if programmed early enough, can yield results that contribute to pre-planning reports. Otherwise, a watching brief is only specified when remains are deemed to be of low significance. The specification normally enables archaeologists to stop contractors' works within reason to retrieve remains and make archaeological records. A watching brief is commonly specified for example on linear projects such as pipelines and roads, on projects where excavation would not be safe or practical, such as when installing secant pile guide trenches or other temporary works, or where archaeologists are overseeing the implementation of an agreed preservation *in situ* programme (see below):

  - **excavation:** excavation may be specified (Section 2.3.3) to enable archaeologists to make a permanent record of the deposits, features, structures and finds that they remove

  - **underwater excavation:** in some cases physical intervention is necessary to determine the nature, date, or extent of underwater remains (for example the removal of finds or timber samples, or the removal of sand/silts)

  - **standing building analysis and recording:** although outside the scope of this document, it should be noted that detailed records of standing historic structures may be required and are often most cost-effectively carried out at the same time as subsurface archaeological work to create an integrated record. Techniques may include measured survey, photogrammetry, 3D laser scanning and other techniques.

Figure 2.9   *Trial trenching on a rural site (courtesy MoLAS)*

2.3.3   Mitigation options: preservation *in situ*, replacement by record or both

Mitigation is the term archaeologists and planning authorities use to describe the agreed archaeological response to a development proposal. That response, whether to protect or to investigate archaeological remains, is the means of mitigating the potentially damaging impact of development on the finite archaeological resource.

The agreed mitigation for any development proposal affecting archaeological remains should be set out in detail in an approved method statement, or written scheme of investigation (WSI), also referred to as the archaeological project design. This document is likely to form part of the formal contract documentation regulating the archaeological work and will require approval by the planning authority.

1   Preservation of archaeological remains *in situ*:

This is seen in current planning policy as good practice and may be a requirement for all nationally important heritage assets whether they are legally protected or not. In any event, the policy (PPG16) is based on a presumption in favour of preservation *in situ*. Reasonable effort should be made to avoid disturbing important archaeological remains, for example by altering the arrangement of buildings and open areas, by adopting less intrusive foundation or basement designs, or by the avoidance of development on certain sites on a linear project.

Compromises may be achieved by negotiation whereby some areas are preserved *in situ*, while other areas are excavated as a representative sample of deposits that will be destroyed by development. For current practice see Davis *et al* (2004), Nixon (2004) and English Heritage (2007b).

In some instances it may be a formal requirement that important archaeological remains are preserved for display, rather than left undisturbed below the ground.

2   Excavation (of some or all of the site):

Archaeological excavation enables the *in situ* resource to be investigated and replaced by a durable and accessible record. Described in PPG16 as preservation by record this concept is now increasingly referred to as replacement by record. The IFA defines excavation as:

> "a programme of controlled, intrusive fieldwork with defined research objectives which examines, records and interprets archaeological deposits, features and structures and, as appropriate, retrieves artefacts, ecofacts and other remains within a specified area or site on land, intertidal zone or underwater. The records made and objects gathered during fieldwork are studied and the results of that study published in detail appropriate to the project design. The purpose of excavation is to examine the archaeological resource within a given area or site within a framework of defined research objectives, to seek a better understanding of and compile a lasting record of that resource, to analyse and interpret the results, and disseminate them"

(IFA, 2001b).

A lasting record refers to the creation, storage and curation of the site archive and dissemination refers to publication of the results of fieldwork.

Figure 2.10
Excavation in progress on complex urban deposits (courtesy MoLAS)

2.4 WHO DOES WHAT IN THE HISTORIC ENVIRONMENT SECTOR?

2.4.1 Specialist advice and services for developers

There are over 6000 archaeologists working in the UK, either as individuals or as part of organisations. There are around 40 large archaeological practices that provide contracting and consultancy services and several public and private sector enterprises specialising in small projects or particular types of project or technical expertise. There are also several multi-disciplinary organisations in the construction sector that have professional archaeologists on their staff. Most organisations offering consultancy advice are private sector enterprises: contracting services may be offered by private sector companies or trusts, or by public sector bodies based in universities or local government.

♦   consultants provide independent expert advice to the development sector. Their work focuses on risk assessments and design services and, as with other professional consultants, they often negotiate on behalf of clients with local government and heritage agencies. They also undertake archaeological research and mitigation design. It is possible for a contractor to be hired as a consultant or for advice to be provided by planning archaeologists. It is important that archaeologists hired as consultants provide adequate assurances regarding the impartiality of their advice and declare any potential conflict of interest

♦   contractors undertake archaeological research and mitigation including documentary, fieldwork and laboratory studies. They may provide a wide range of specialist services including project management, excavation, conservation, historical research, botanical and zoological analysis, finds study, metallurgy, survey, illustration, editing and publication

♦   professional institute: in a profession that works for both the public and the private sector, there is a need for a strong, authoritative body to ensure effective self-regulation. This role is fulfilled by the Institute of Field Archaeologists (IFA), a professional membership institution with strict peer reviewed entrance requirements and CPD standards. Its members, which include individuals as well as registered archaeological organisations, are bound by by-laws codifying professional ethics, and follow the IFA standards and guidance (see IFA, 2002, 2005a and 2005b).

2.4.2   National government bodies and their advisors

Archaeological advisors and specialist heritage officers in government, statutory and other regulatory offices are commonly referred to within the historic environment sector as curators, for their role and responsibility of caring for the *in situ* archaeological resource.

Most regulatory and curatorial aspects of archaeology have been devolved to the UK (see Appendix A1 for contact details):

England:	The lead department for policy is the Department of Culture, Media and Sport (DCMS), taking advice from its agency English Heritage.
Scotland:	The Royal Commission on the Ancient and Historical Monuments of Scotland (RCAHMS) is responsible for the survey and record of the historic environment including the curation and maintenance of its collections, formerly referred to as the National Monuments Record of Scotland (NMRS), and Historic Scotland is the relevant part of the Scottish Executive.
Wales:	Responsibility for the historic record lies with the Royal Commission on the Ancient and Historical Monuments of Wales (RCAHMW) or Comisiwn Brenhinol Henebion Cymru (CBHC). Cadw is the arm of Welsh Assembly government responsible for protecting and promoting the heritage of Wales.

Northern Ireland: The role of conserving and protecting the natural and built environment in Northern Ireland is fulfilled by the Northern Ireland Environment Agency.

The remit of each national body varies slightly, but generally includes advising government on the historic environment, conserving and enhancing the historic environment (through designation, advice, grant aid and management of historic properties), and broadening public access to and understanding of the past (through education and research).

The English government's policy regarding the historic environment is detailed in *The historic environment: a force for our future* (DCMS, 2001).

2.4.3   Regional government

The remit of regional government in archaeology is yet to be fully defined, although there is a significant role through regional spatial strategies. English Heritage has adopted a regionalised structure and there are moves for DoE's Northern Ireland Environment Agency to follow. Scotland does not have local authority regions, but has councils, or council areas, that are unitary authorities. Historic Scotland aligns much of its activity so that its area teams cover groups of council areas. In Wales there are four regional archaeological trusts.

2.4.4   Local government

Local government archaeology services have input into local authority museums, educational, and cultural and leisure strategies, and they are responsible for providing advice to the local planning authority.

Regulation and advice concerning archaeology at the level of county, unitary, or local authority is provided by an archaeology service, planning archaeologist or archaeology officer (also termed curator). Contact details for local government curators are available from their professional association's website: <http://www.algao.org.uk/>.

These curators are responsible for the management and protection of the archaeological resource, maintain the Historic Environment Record (HER), or Sites and Monuments Record (SMR). They also work with others bodies to devise regional research frameworks.

All local planning authorities are required to have access to conservation and design skills. Local authority historic environment or archaeology services are non-statutory, though the Heritage Protection White Paper (DCMS/WAG, 2007) indicates that it will become a statutory responsibility for local authorities in England and Wales to provide or have access to a Historic Environment Record and expert advice. At present there is near complete coverage. For England, visit the HER website for contact detail information: <http://www.heritagegateway.org.uk>.

Through planning controls local authorities are responsible for the conservation of 98 per cent of the historic environment including listed buildings, archaeological sites and monuments, historic landscapes, historic parks and gardens and historic battlefields. Local authorities also work in partnership with (and should consult) the relevant national agency on the conservation of what are presently termed Grade I, Grade II* and Grade II (or Grade A and B in Scotland) listed buildings.

Scheduled Monuments (the other two per cent) are protected by separate legislation, and applicants should seek consent from the relevant Secretary of State, applying through the inspector of ancient monuments for the relevant region. In future this may change in England and Wales so that all applications for works to or on a registered historic asset will be through the local authority planning department.

Initially advice should be sought from local authority curators and at the earliest possible stage in developing a proposal to achieve quality results with efficient use of resources.

Many local authorities also issue supplementary planning guidance (SPGs) explaining how national planning policy relating to the archaeology and the historic environment is interpreted and implemented by the local planning authority.

Conservation officer: the county, unitary, or local authority officer responsible for advising on issues of building conservation, countryside/conservation officers are involved in the management, protection and improvement of the local environment. This usually includes putting into practice schemes to conserve existing features, restore degraded landscapes or create new landscapes. Conservation officers also input to Environmental Impact Assessments and field surveys, and are responsible for Tree Preservation Orders etc.

Archaeology officer: the archaeologist employed by the local authority as the curatorial archaeologist responsible for that local government area. In England local government archaeologists may also be appointed at district and unitary authority levels. These other areas of local government may also be catered for by the county archaeologist and associated staff, either directly or indirectly. The county archaeologist should always be available for advice on any archaeological matter in the county and is responsible for the HER/SMR. The district archaeology officer advises the district planning authority on the potential impact of development on archaeological deposits and recommends appropriate mitigation strategies. The archaeology officer can provide initial advice on:

◆ whether or not significant deposits may be present at an application site

◆ the mitigation measures that may be applied (but not on the cost of such measures)

◆ details of commercial archaeological organisations that might be commissioned to undertake works.

The archaeology officers will produce an outline framework of the archaeological situation that a developer has to address together with an indication of the scope of works that will be required.

The following arrangements apply in particular parts of the UK:

◆ in the Greater London Area, the City of London and the London Borough of Southwark have their own curator (archaeology officer). In the other London boroughs archaeological advice is provided by English Heritage's Greater London Archaeological Advisory Service (GLAAS) <http://www.english-heritage.org.uk>

◆ the 10 Greater Manchester district authorities are provided with archaeological advice by the Greater Manchester Archaeological Unit (GMAU): <http://www.agma.gov.uk/ccm/agma/Units/Greater_Manchester_Archaelogical_Unit.en>

◆ similar arrangements exist for the other metropolitan areas (for example, South Yorkshire, West Yorkshire, Merseyside). Check Heritage Gateway for contact details: <http://www.heritagegateway.org.uk>

Archaeology and development

- national park authorities in England have their own archaeological curators <http://www.algao.org.uk>, while the Welsh national parks are covered by the regional archaeological trusts and in Scotland by local authority curators or the regional archaeology service. There are as yet no national parks in Northern Ireland

- the 12 West of Scotland local authorities (Argyll & Bute, East Ayrshire, East Renfrewshire, Glasgow City, Inverclyde, North Ayrshire, North Lanarkshire, Renfrewshire, South Ayrshire, South Lanarkshire, West Dunbartonshire and West Lothian), and one national park (Loch Lomond and the Trossachs) are provided with archaeological advice by the West of Scotland Archaeology Service <http://www.wosas.org.uk>

- in Wales archaeological advice is provided to the planning authorities by the four regional archaeological trusts, which act as curators on their behalf:

  - Archaeoleg Cambria (Cambria Archaeology) <http://www.cambria.org.uk>

  - Ymddiriedolaeth Archaeolegol Morgannwg-Gwent (Glamorgan Gwent Archaeological Trust) <http://www.ggat.org.uk>

  - Ymddiriedolaeth Archaeolegol Clwyd-Powys (Clwyd-Powys Archaeological Trust) <http://www.cpat.org.uk>

  - Ymddiriedolaeth Archaeolegol Gwynedd (Gwynedd Archaeological Trust) <http://www.heneb.co.uk>

- in Northern Ireland, the Northern Ireland Office acts as a unitary authority for the entire province. The Northern Ireland Environment Agency (see Section 2.4.2) is responsible for advising the planning service regarding planning issues in relation to archaeology, listed buildings and conservation areas.

2.4.5   The voluntary sector

Various voluntary archaeological organisations exist across the UK – principally local and national societies (eg Devon Archaeological Society, Society for Medieval Archaeology), and pressure groups. The Council for British Archaeology (CBA, <http://www.britarch.ac.uk>) plays an important role, among many other responsibilities, in supporting such groups. Many societies produce learned journals, and these are some of the most important publication outlets for the results of archaeological work. Voluntary groups may engage in fieldwork, and a few will undertake small-scale projects for developers. As with paid archaeologists, they should adhere to professional standards, and have the opportunity to demonstrate competence through the IFA.

In the interests of both sustainable communities and good public relations, opportunities should be sought to involve local groups in aspects of archaeological work, after careful assessment of logistical and safety considerations. Advice may be sought from the project's archaeologist, the relevant curators and the health and safety advisor.

2.5   ARCHAEOLOGY LEGISLATION AND PLANNING POLICY

2.5.1   The international context

The management of the interface between archaeological sites and development through heritage and planning law conforms to a wider framework of environmental protection, and within that the protection of the historic environment. An example is the Council of Europe Convention on the Protection of the Archaeological Heritage (Valletta, 1992).

The United Nations Educational Scientific and Cultural Organisation (UNESCO) has responsibility for administering and maintaining the list of World Heritage Sites <http://whc.unesco.org>. World Heritage Sites, defined for their cultural heritage value, are monuments, buildings, sites or areas "which are of outstanding universal value from the historical, aesthetic, ethnological or anthropological point of view" (UNESCO 72). There are now 27 World Heritage Sites of this type in the UK. World Heritage Sites do not yet have additional legal protection, but national regulatory bodies will expect such sites to be protected and managed. Local planning authorities should treat World Heritage Sites as key material concerns in the planning process, and each will have a management plan.

UK planning guidance also conforms to the guidance set out in the International Council on Monuments and Sites *Charter for the protection and management of the archaeological heritage* (ICOMOS, 1990), which states that "the protection of the archaeological heritage should be considered as a moral obligation upon all human beings; it is also a collective public responsibility".

2.5.2 UK designation of archaeological sites and their legal protection

Certain archaeological sites are protected in law. They are:

1   **Scheduled Monuments (Scheduled Monuments in England and Scheduled Ancient Monuments in Scotland and Wales).** Under the Ancient Monuments and Archaeological Areas Act 1979, Scheduled Monument consent is required for any works involving "demolishing, destroying, damaging, removing, repairing, altering, adding to, flooding or tipping material onto the monument". Certain existing or seasonal operations (eg gardening or defined agricultural activities) may be permitted by existing prior agreements (known as class consent). The preparation of a project design and supporting documentation required for consent is a specialist archaeological matter, so skilled advice should be sought. Consent cannot be granted retrospectively.

Key guidance: Scheduled Monument consent

It is a criminal offence, potentially leading to fines or imprisonment, to:

◆ carry out any unauthorised works on a Scheduled Monument (ie without consent)

◆ cause damage to a Scheduled Monument (Case study 2.1)

◆ fail to adhere to the terms of consent.

Development or construction works that affect a Scheduled Monument require formal permission (Scheduled Monument consent).

Scheduled Monument consent cannot be granted retrospectively.

The granting of Scheduled Monument consent does not imply planning permission, or vice versa.

Applications for Scheduled Monument consent are made:

◆ in England to the Department of Culture Media and Sport (application forms should be obtained from and any proposed work discussed with the relevant English Heritage inspector of ancient monuments)

◆ in Northern Ireland the Northern Ireland Environment Agency

◆ in Scotland to Historic Scotland

◆ in Wales to Cadw.

Archaeology and development

Background

In the late 1980s, construction of an office development was underway at Cannon Street Station, London, a site known to overlie important Roman buildings and waterfronts designated as a Scheduled Monument. Only limited below-ground works were proposed and these were given Scheduled Monument consent, subject to an intervention by the Museum of London. In the course of the development additional drainage works became necessary, including a deep inspection chamber, which was constructed without a revised consent application or archaeological intervention.

Outcome

The principal contractor was prosecuted for causing works to be executed damaging a Scheduled Monument, found guilty and fined £1000 with £20 000 costs.

Lessons learned

◆ always take professional advice, obtain the relevant consents and follow good practice guidance before undertaking works that might affect a Scheduled Monument.

(source: MoLAS)

2   **Listed buildings.** The Planning (Listed Buildings and Conservation Areas) Act 1990 and related legislation impose a duty on national governments to compile lists of buildings of special architectural or historic interest. In England and Wales, buildings are assigned to Grade I, Grade II* and Grade II, in Scotland Grades A, B and C(S) are used and in Northern Ireland Grades A, B+ and B in decreasing order of their relative significance. The statutory bodies responsible for listed buildings are English Heritage (England), Cadw (Wales), Historic Scotland (Scotland), the Northern Ireland Environment Agency (Northern Ireland). Any works involving the demolition, alteration, or extension of a listed building that would affect its character as a listed building require consent from the relevant statutory body. Proposals that may affect the setting of listed buildings are required to have special regard to the desirability of preserving that setting.

Key guidance: listed building consent and conservation area consent

It is a criminal offence potentially leading to fines or imprisonment, to alter, extend or demolish a listed building without listed building consent.

The need for consent applies to all parts of the building, interior and exterior, even if not mentioned in the official list description. It may also apply to associated buildings (ie within the curtilage of the principal building) including boundary walls (see English Heritage, 2004).

Consent may be needed for works on structures within a conservation area. Advice should be sought from the local planning authority.

There will be a presumption in favour of the physical preservation of the listed building.

Applications for listed building consent and conservation area consent should be made to the local planning authority.

3   **Conservation areas.** Section 69 of the Planning (Listed Buildings and Conservation Areas) Act 1990 and related legislation imposes a duty on local planning authorities (or the Department of the Environment in Northern Ireland) to designate as conservation areas any area of special architectural or historic interest, the character or appearance of which it is desirable to preserve or enhance. In Scotland, Chapter 9 of the Planning (Listed Buildings and Conservation Areas) (Scotland) Act 1997 applies. Certain archaeological sites lie within conservation areas, and there may be additional restrictions on alterations to non-listed

structures, felling of trees, or permitted development. Most planning authorities issue their own supplementary planning guidance on development and planning in a conservation area.

4   **Designated wrecks.** Section 1 of the Protection of Wrecks Act 1973 provides protection to some 60 wrecks around the UK, designated for their archaeological and historical significance. The administration of this Act and the issue of licenses allowing diving, survey, collection of objects or excavation on these sites is the responsibility of English Heritage (England), Cadw (Wales), Historic Scotland (Scotland) and the Northern Ireland Environment Agency (Northern Ireland). Note that under the Merchant Shipping Act 1995 finders of wrecks and those engaged in salvage (which may include archaeological materials) are obliged to declare it to the Maritime and Coastguard Agency's Receiver of Wreck <http://www.mcga.gov.uk> (see also English Heritage, 2002 and 2006).

5   **Designated vessels and controlled sites.** Certain military aircraft crash sites and military shipwrecks are designated and protected under the Protection of Military Remains Act 1986. These sites are administered by the Ministry of Defence.

6   **Archaeological sites.** These may lie within areas designated as historic parks and gardens and battlefields. Such designation brings no additional statutory protection, but local authorities are required to prepare policies promoting the conservation of such sites and to treat them as material considerations in the planning process.

Changes to designations (England and Wales)

Government ministers are usually responsible for designating historic assets (such as Scheduled Monuments or listed buildings), though in England this role may in future pass to English Heritage.

Following publication of the Heritage Protection White Paper (DCMS/WAG 2007), in April 2008 government issued the Draft Heritage Protection Bill, setting out significant changes to the legal protection of designated historic assets in England and Wales. The key provisions are:

◆ a single register, bringing together listed buildings, Scheduled Monuments, registered parks, gardens and battlefields

◆ unification of listed building and Scheduled Monument consent regimes, with responsibility for consents given to local authorities

◆ introduction of optional heritage partnership agreements between the owners of a site, local authorities and English Heritage to be employed as alternative proactive management regimes

◆ a statutory right of appeal to the Secretary of State on decisions to designate a site.

The proposals are not intended to strengthen or weaken the present regimes, but to make them more transparent, consistent and easier to operate efficiently alongside the planning process.

Archaeology and development

2.5.3   Burials and human remains

In England and Wales, disturbance of human remains may be authorised by act of Parliament, Home Office Licence (through the Ministry of Justice), or Church of England Faculty (English Heritage, 2005). The Northern Ireland Environment Agency issue such licences and the Church of Ireland such faculties (IAI, 2004). Under Scots Law there is no such system of authorisation (see key guidance and Historic Scotland, 2006a).

Key guidance: burials and human remains

◆ human remains should always be treated with dignity and respect

◆ burials should not be disturbed without good reason. However, the demands of the modern world are such that it may be necessary to disturb burials in advance of development

◆ human remains, and the archaeological evidence for the rites that accompanied their burial, are important sources of scientific information

◆ there is a need to acknowledge the feelings and views of living family members when known

◆ there is a need for decisions to be made in the public interest, and in an accountable way (English Heritage and the Church of England, 2005).

The need for assessment and advice: the law concerning burials varies across the UK. If there is any likelihood that human remains may be encountered during construction specialist archaeological advice should be sought on obtaining proper legal authority to disturb them.

Accidental disturbance: in all cases of accidental disturbance site work in the area should be stopped, the police should be informed immediately and it is important to inform the local curator and seek specialist archaeological advice on the potential legal and scientific consequences of the discovery.

Figure 2.11

The unexpected discovery of human remains can cause delays (courtesy MoLAS)

In England, disturbance of human remains may be allowed by the Act of Parliament authorising a specific major project, but otherwise the following legislation applies:

◆ Town and Country Planning (Churches, Places of Religious Worship and Burial Grounds) Regulations 1950

◆ Disused Burial Grounds Act 1884

- Disused Burial Grounds (Amendment) Act 1981
- Burial Act 1857.

Specific guidance in relation to archaeology and the implementation of the Disused Burial Grounds Acts may be issued by the Ministry of Justice.

Certain areas and buildings owned by churches fall outside the normal legal and planning process – specifically parish churches, churchyards, consecrated ground and cathedral land. The situation in Northern Ireland is broadly similar. Although much of the legislation relates specifically to Christian burials, non-Christian or pre-Christian human remains are afforded the same legal protection. More detailed advice has been produced by English Heritage and the Church of England (2005) and by the Institute of Archaeologists of Ireland (IAI, 2004).

The position in Scots Law has been effectively summarised in *The treatment of human remains in archaeology* (Historic Scotland, 2006a). There is no faculty or licence system as in England, but it is normal practice to check with the procurator fiscal that no offence would be committed under laws relating to public decency or the violation of sepulchres provisions, and a warrant may be sought to this effect.

2.5.4   Treasure and the ownership of archaeological objects

In England and Wales landowners retain all rights of ownership to archaeological materials found on their land, except items classed as treasure under the Treasure Act 1996 (see below). However, it is good practice for a developer to sign a transfer of title form assigning ownership of all archaeological finds to the intended archive repository, preferably before starting any work on the site (although it may be acceptable for this to occur while the archive is being prepared for deposition, see Section 4.7.5). The eventual repository of the site archive should be identified in the early stages of a project, and identified in project briefs and specifications. In the event of the chance discovery of archaeological finds (those not covered by the Act) on a site where no professional archaeological consultant or contractor is in place, it is good practice to report such discoveries to the local curator and under the voluntary portable antiquities scheme <http://www.finds.org.uk/> to one of its regional finds liaison officers.

In Northern Ireland, all archaeological excavations are licensed. The Environment Agency issue transfer of title forms to licensees, who have a responsibility to secure the signature of the landowner. These forms transfer title of excavated material to the Department of the Environment, on the understanding that the material would be offered to the Ulster Museum. Non-excavation (ie unlicensed) projects expected to produce a material archive (such as field walking) also require arrangements for archive repository and transfer of title to be finalised before the project starts. Under the Historic Monuments and Archaeological Objects (Northern Ireland) Order 1995 it is a statutory duty of finders to report all archaeological objects to the Environment Agency, the director of the Ulster Museum, or the officer in charge of a police station, within 14 days of discovery, unless the finds have been made in the course of a licensed excavation. Issues of title may then be resolved as appropriate.

In Scotland all archaeological artefacts may be claimed as the property of the Crown. All such finds must be reported to the Scottish Archaeological Finds Allocation Panel. If the finds came from a project funded by Historic Scotland, they should initially be reported to Historic Scotland who then report to the Scottish Archaeological Finds Allocation Panel (Historic Scotland, 2001). This body determines which archive repository will have responsibility for, and assume ownership of, the material archive.

The Treasure Act 1996 requires finds in England and Wales to be reported to the coroner within 14 days of the finder realising the find may be of treasure status. It is an offence under the Act, carrying a maximum penalty of three months imprisonment or a fine of £5000 or both, not to report finds. The Treasure Act places restrictions on the release of information about the location of any find, particularly in advance of an inquest (DCMS, 2000). For the purposes of this Act treasure is defined as:

◆ all objects other than coins that are at least 300 years old with at least 10 per cent gold or silver

◆ all coins from the same find, provided they are at least 300 years old with 10 per cent gold or silver (if less that 10 per cent there should be more than 10 coins)

◆ all objects found in association with the above

◆ base metal deposits of prehistoric date.

All finds made on the seashore, intertidal zone or seabed in UK waters may potentially be classified as wreck and under the Merchant Shipping Act 1995 should be reported to the receiver of wreck at the Maritime and Coastguard Agency <http://www.mcga.gov.uk>.

Good practice: archaeological finds and records

It is good practice for the integrity of the archive (finds, paper record, photographic record, digital record) produced by a site or an archaeological project to be maintained to the benefit of future generations.

In this context, finds means all recovered artefacts and environmental remains, or a sub-sample thereof agreed by local curators and the designated repository, with regard to national guidelines.

For a developer, the completion of the archive marks the end of the final stage of post-excavation work (Section 4.7.5) and is the point at which planning authorities should sign off archaeological conditions.

2.5.5   Planning policy and controls relating to archaeology

In England, there are eight regional spatial strategies that concern the historic environment. Policies relating to the historic environment are also set out in local authority development plans and in the core strategies and area action plans required in local development frameworks (as set out in PPS12).

Guidance on planning and archaeology is offered in a range of policy guidance notes, covering government policy on archaeological remains on land, and how they should be preserved or recorded both in an urban setting and in the countryside. These guidance notes provide advice on the treatment of archaeological remains and discoveries under the development plan and control systems, including the weight to be given to them in planning decisions and the use of planning conditions (see *Bibliography*). They are:

◆ England

❖ Planning Policy Guidance 15: *Planning and the historic environment*

❖ Planning Policy Guidance 16: *Archaeology and planning*

◆ Scotland

❖ National Planning Policy Guideline (NPPG) 5: *Archaeology and planning*

❖ Planning Advice Note (PAN) 42: *Archaeology – the planning process and scheduled monument procedures*

- Wales
  - Planning Policy Wales
  - Technical Advice Note (Wales) 6: *Archaeology and planning*
- Northern Ireland
  - Planning policy statement (PPS) 6: *Planning, archaeology and the built heritage.*

Key guidance: archaeology and planning controls

UK planning guidance states that:

- the presence of archaeological remains, even on non-designated sites, will be regarded as a material consideration in the planning process and should be adequately assessed, as with other environmental constraints, such as contamination, or wildlife
- any potential damage to important archaeological remains by development or construction is viewed as a significant environmental impact
- any such potential impact requires formal impact assessment and that mitigation measures should be identified and implemented with funding from the developer.

This applies equally to commercial and charitable developments (such as registered social landlords).

For certain types of development a formal Environmental Impact Assessment may be necessary (Section 4.3.3).

In any event it is considered the developer's responsibility to provide a competent professional assessment of the potential impact of development on archaeological remains in support of the development proposals. This may require a desk-based assessment and/or a programme of trial work (evaluation) to be conducted before an application can be determined. Statements on the measures to mitigate potential damage may also be required.

Planning permission may be refused where applications do not have due regard to local planning objectives. This may concern the mitigation of damage to or destruction of archaeological sites by eliminating or reducing disturbance, or by allowing (destructive) archaeological investigation, analysis and dissemination of the findings.

2.5.6   Outside the normal planning process

Certain landowners, institutions and types of development fall outside the normal planning process. Potential archaeological risks should be anticipated, assessed and managed.

1. **The Crown Estate.** The Crown is a large landowner, with assets that include some 50 per cent of the UK foreshore and most of the seabed out to the territorial limit (including many ports and the administration of licenses for marine aggregate dredging). The Crown Estate requires developers to provide archaeological assessment and mitigation in line with the policy of UK national governments.

2. **Infrastructure projects.** Individual infrastructure projects may run through several local authority areas, requiring multiple consultations and making unified archaeological curation difficult. The largest projects may be outside normal planning procedures, either authorised by specific legislation (such as the Channel Tunnel Rail Link, highways built under the Highways Act 1980) or designated as a major infrastructure project (MIP) by the Secretary of State for Communities and Local Government. Consideration of archaeological assessment and mitigation as part of an Environmental Impact Assessment is still required.

Archaeology and development

3   **Ecclesiastical developments.** In England and Wales ecclesiastical buildings in use for ecclesiastical purposes are exempt from listed building and conservation area controls (the Ecclesiastical Exemption (Listed Buildings and Conservation Areas) Order 1994). This ecclesiastical exemption applies to the following denominations only:

❖ Church of England

❖ Church in Wales

❖ Roman Catholic Church

❖ Methodist Church

❖ Baptist Union of Great Britain

❖ Baptist Union of Wales

❖ United Reformed Church.

Each denomination is obliged to have its own system of development control and to protect archaeological and architectural remains. In Northern Ireland all churches and chapels are exempt, but in Scotland, under a voluntary scheme reviewed every three years, works to the exterior of a listed ecclesiastical building should have agreement from the local planning authority and Historic Scotland. Detailed advice is provided in English Heritage (2003a) and Historic Scotland (2006b). In England, ecclesiastical exemption is under review and protection/ management of exempt sites may in future be secured by Heritage Partnership Agreements (HPAs) negotiated between the owners, the local authority and English Heritage (DCMS, 2006a).

4   **General permitted development orders.** Developers and those engaged in agriculture and forestry have the right to carry out certain limited forms of development without the need to make an application for planning permission, as granted under the terms of the Town and Country Planning (General Permitted Development) Order 1995. However, those undertaking such work are obliged to consult with the local planning authority to determine whether archaeological remains may be present, and to allow access to an archaeologist nominated by the planning authority. If an area of archaeological interest is present, applicants should secure a programme of archaeological work in accordance with a written scheme of investigation, submitted by the applicant and approved in writing by the planning authority.

5   **Works by statutory undertakers.** Works by gas, water, electricity and other utility providers are governed by their own legislation and may fall outside normal planning control as permitted development subject to monitoring by local authorities. It is good practice for statutory undertakers to take specialist advice as to the potential archaeological impacts of proposed works. Utility companies are increasingly applying the principles of national government guidance (key guidance, Section 2.5.5) to their larger projects, and operate good practice standards in accordance with relevant utility legislation.

2.5.7   Excavation licensing in Northern Ireland

In Northern Ireland, all archaeological excavations should be carried out under the direction of a qualified archaeologist, licensed by the Northern Ireland Environment Agency (Section 2.4.2). A licence application must be submitted for every excavation, by the archaeologist who will direct the work, at least three weeks before the date when work is due to start. Any search (eg metal detecting, field walking) for archaeological objects (ie finds) also requires a license.

In England, Wales and Scotland no such licensing scheme is in operation.

3   Archaeological risk

This section provides an introduction to the identification, assessment and management of archaeological risk to avoid, reduce and/or control the impact of archaeology on a development.

Detailed practical advice on risk assessment and risk management follows in Chapter 4, with an in depth guide to the stages of archaeological work within the construction process. Examples of how risk can be turned to opportunity are also given in this chapter.

3.1   PRINCIPLES

Archaeological remains are just one of many factors that can influence and potentially threaten the business case for development. Unmanaged archaeological remains can affect financial, commercial, legal, programming and reputation outcomes.

Key guidance: what is archaeological risk?

In risk terms, archaeological remains should be considered as hazards which, if not properly anticipated and planned for, may cause an adverse effect on the desired outcome (in this case, a successful development). So archaeological risk is the potential for archaeological remains or other cultural heritage assets – on, beneath or adjacent to a site – to impose constraints, costs and/or delays, and/or to affect reputation.

Like any other risk archaeological risk can be anticipated and managed, and often avoided.

Why manage archaeological risk?

Applying a simple risk management process benefits all parties and can enable land acquisition, planning, design and development to proceed with increased certainty.

Importantly, archaeologists and the historic environment sector have embraced the risk management approach as a means of integrating archaeological work successfully with modern development. The different stages of archaeological work aim to identify, assess and manage archaeological risk. Archaeologists have drawn parallels with and learned lessons from the approach to managing development on contaminated land.

Similarities in the approaches to managing archaeology and contaminated land issues include:

♦ both are a significant below-ground issue

♦ both require specialist data collection and analyses to allow qualitative and quantitative risk assessments

♦ both can be difficult to predict with certainty (residual risk profile)

♦ both can be time consuming and costly to deal with

♦ both have an associated liability for the analysis and publication of results (archaeology being similar to full and proper disposal of contaminated remains).

Note that costs for dealing with archaeology may be tax efficient where combined with contaminated land remediation tax relief.

Figure 3.1 illustrates how the main archaeological and development stages relate to each other.

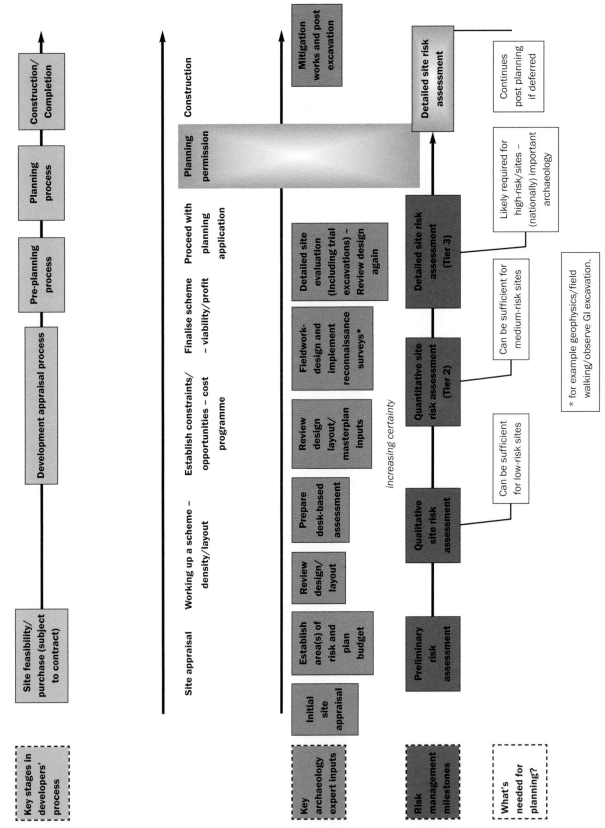

Figure 3.1   Diagram showing archaeology risk management and the developers' process with key inputs from different professionals (courtesy Scott Wilson Ltd)

Note: The diagram emphasises the increasing certainty that is gained from comprehensive risk assessment. The focus for developers is to understand the key below-ground issues before planning and to make sure buried archaeological remains are considered sufficiently early to influence design. This provides cost effective management against expensive redesign costs or design limitations becoming an issue when determining the process of a viable project. Consultation with heritage advisors in local and national government should take place at all stages to ensure that decision makers have sufficient information at the determination stage. Also please note that non-intrusive surveys and detailed site evaluations usually take place post determination but sometimes may take place before planning in the most sensitive situations.

A developer should seek appropriate specialist expertise at the earliest opportunity, to identify hazards and risks (both negative and positive) and to plan a programme of archaeological risk management. The professional advisor's role is to guide the developer from site acquisition and land assembly through to implementation and completion, by assessing and mitigating risks to the development and negotiating outcomes on the developer's behalf with statutory bodies and third parties.

3.2   ARCHAEOLOGY AS A DEVELOPMENT COST

Archaeological works in the UK can be time consuming and expensive. To illustrate maximum figures, research commissioned by the City of London Corporation indicated that for a major central London development with complex archaeological remains, total archaeological costs may comprise between one and three per cent of construction costs (Corporation of London, 2001). For other developments, particularly outside south-east England, the total is usually less than one per cent. Costs may be proportionally higher in the initial stages of projects, during investigative works before determining a planning application.

Archaeological costs include off-site works, namely the costs for post-excavation assessment, analysis and publication of the results and the deposition of the project archive in a suitable repository. Post-excavation work (including publication and archive deposition) commonly cost the same as on-site works.

In the UK developers are expected to meet the cost of mitigating potential development impacts on archaeological remains (Section 2.5). Decisions on archaeological strategies imposed by local authority curators will depend on the potential significance of the archaeological remains rather than their cost to developers.

The national heritage bodies may sometimes offer financial assistance for the investigation of nationally important sites in imminent and unavoidable danger of destruction. However, the limited available funding tends to go to sites threatened by natural forces, for example coastal erosion, rather than development, or to projects with significant potential to illuminate important archaeological research questions. Rarely, support may be given to non-profit organisations (Case study 3.1).

Case study 3.1   *Financial support from a heritage body*

Background

In Dover, Orbit Housing Association commissioned trial excavations covering four per cent of a steep hillside site close to a known Saxon cemetery, and found evidence for scattered Saxon burials. The professional team's judgement was that intensive burial would not be expected on the site because of the steep terrain. Later excavations demonstrated that the cemetery had extended across the hillside and 250 graves had to be recorded, excavated, analysed and published.

Outcome

Because the Housing Association had carefully followed planning advice with regard to the assessment of archaeology, and the find was unexpected, unlikely, and important, English Heritage agreed to fund part of the post-excavation analysis (some £53 000). Additional help was provided by the British Museum.

Lessons learned

◆ even when professional archaeological advice has been taken, unexpected remains may sometimes be encountered in the course of groundworks

◆ in exceptional cases, financial support may be available from one of the heritage bodies.

(source: IFA, 1998)

Archaeological consultants and contractors should be able to offer advice on likely costs in relation to specific development proposals. Developers may also wish to consult the guidance on pricing and valuation of archaeological work in Appendix 2 of the ICE guidance notes (ICE, 2004b).

3.3 KEYS TO SUCCESSFUL ARCHAEOLOGICAL RISK

Key guidance: typical archaeology risks faced by development plans

- planning constraints and potential for spot listing and scheduling of remains
- unforeseen or unexpected archaeological remains affecting design, implementation programme and profit margins.

Effective risk management can successfully mitigate the following:

- financial cost overrun:
  - project delays
  - direct archaeology costs
  - re-design costs (and sometimes abortive construction costs)
- commercial impacts:
  - completion delay
  - asset value devaluation
  - devaluation of corporate reputation
  - cancellation
  - legislative constraints.

Key guidance: positive and negative risk assessment

Archaeological risk management should focus on an early understanding of likely outcomes. Developers should seek to understand:

- legal and planning constraints – initial identification of all known constraints
- financial impacts – the likely total direct and indirect financial costs on the project (using risk register and min-max scenarios)
- commercial and design issues – whether archaeological remains may affect the commercial viability of the project, both negatively (eg by reducing the land available for development) and positively (eg by enhancing profile)
- programme implications – whether timing constraints may affect planning, access or development programmes (eg where lack of access may delay essential surveys)
- reputational risks – the likelihood of public or stakeholder interest generating publicity or affecting reputation either positively, or negatively if not dealt with effectively
- other positive risks – the potential to exploit archaeological issues to deliver a positive impact, to the advantage of the development and its stakeholders, whether shareholders, occupants, government, local interest groups or the general public.

3.3.1 Procuring specialist advice and services

Statutory advice from National Heritage Bodies and local planning archaeologists necessarily focuses on implementing conservation policies and managing the risk to archaeological remains from construction. Statutory bodies rarely have the resources to provide detailed information that addresses a developer's archaeological risks. So it is recommended that an independent consultant or contractor is appointed to manage the process and to consult with statutory bodies on the developer's behalf.

It is good practice for developers to seek specialist archaeological advice at the earliest opportunity.

Local government archaeology officers or their equivalents (Section 2.4.4) and the relevant heritage bodies (Section 2.4.2) should be able to give general advice on archaeology within their local area and inform developers' preliminary research into the suitability of a particular site for development before planning application. A developer should not rely solely on local authority archaeological advice.

A developer should procure the services of an appropriately qualified and experienced professional who can assess archaeological risk, work with the professional team during the feasibility and design stages and negotiate on the developer's behalf with local and statutory authorities.

Key guidance: online sources to identify known archaeological sites

Information about known archaeological sites and access to historic environment records and databases can be found at:

England <http://www.magic.gov.uk> and <http://www.heritagegateway.org.uk>

Scotland <http://www.rcahms.gov.uk/>

Wales <http://www.coflein.gov.uk>

Note: these online sources are not a substitute for seeking specialist professional advice. They are unlikely to include unknown archaeological remains, and will not give any indication of development control advice.

Individual developers will decide whether to use an independent archaeological consultant or a consultant/project manager attached to the contractor. Using an independent consultant may be a way of ensuring impartial advice, or to provide oversight and management control of archaeological programme and costs, particularly in the case of complex or lengthy projects. Other developers may prefer to procure specialist advice directly from archaeological contractors. In any event, the developer should base the decision on an assessment of the abilities, qualifications and relevant experience of the available advisors, and should integrate the archaeological advisor with the project team.

Note: at present anyone can practice as and call themselves an archaeologist. A wide range of academic qualifications in aspects of archaeology exists, and the vast majority of practising archaeologists are graduates. National Vocational Qualifications in archaeological practice have recently been launched, but until the scheme is widely adopted developers should establish that their appointed archaeological consultants and contractors are suitably competent, qualified and/or experienced in relation to the type of services required.

The professional body for archaeologists, the Institute of Field Archaeologists (IFA), advises that developers should as far as possible procure services from Registered Archaeological Organisations (RAOs) and/or from individual IFA members. RAOs are assessed and regularly inspected by their peers, and are obliged to apply every two years to re-register. They are bound to working in accordance with the IFA code of conduct (IFA, 2006) and other by-laws and to comply with standards and guidance that establish professional good practice, which local authority archaeologists and planners insist upon. RAOs are subject to sanctions (including expulsion from the register) through a formal complaints procedure. Details of RAOs and individual members of the IFA are published in its yearbook and on its website: <http://www.archaeologists.net>.

Archaeology and development

When appointing an archaeologist, a developer should first ascertain that the organisation or individual:

◆ has understanding and direct experience relevant to the nature and scale of the task in hand

◆ can provide personnel with appropriate skills, qualifications and IFA membership grades for the work

◆ can meet the time constraints

◆ has the infrastructure necessary to support the work in question

◆ can publish the excavation results in an appropriate form (usually in peer-reviewed journals and archaeological monographs) and deposit the project archive in a suitable repository

◆ has a good safety record

◆ will conform to national standards (for example RAO status, individual IFA membership or track record)

◆ has the necessary range of skills to deliver the required services (including in-house specialist skills or established arrangements to contract out as appropriate)

◆ if the site is in Northern Ireland, that they are eligible to apply for a licence.

The developer may wish to check that the archaeologist is approved by the local authority or other curator.

> **Lack of early professional advice can lead to programme delays**
>
> In areas of unknown archaeological importance, it is common for planning conditions to be attached that specify no development should take place before a programme of approved archaeological works has been implemented. If no archaeological assessment was carried out pre-planning, this may be the first time that archaeology is raised as a factor resulting in late changes in the development process that may put unnecessary pressure on the programme.

3.3.2 An integrated design team

The successful integration of archaeology in a development or construction scheme requires a team of a large number of individuals with widely varied specialisms and responsibilities.

To manage risk, key liaison issues are contracts, costs, programme and performance reviews.

The value of mutual understanding between developers and archaeologists has long been recognised. In the UK the the British Archaeologists' and Developers' Liaison Group formed by the British Property Federation and the Standing Conference of Archaeological Unit Managers, first published a code of practice regarding developer-funded archaeology in 1986. To promote effective communication and shared objectives across the design and development team, developers should integrate their archaeological consultants and contractors into their design teams.

3.3.3 Effective communication across the design team and with the relevant authorities

Clear channels of communication and regular meetings are important in this regard, and should be maintained at all stages of a project. A developer may also find it advantageous to establish regular meetings between the archaeological advisor and the planning or other regulatory authority, with the aim of understanding each other's position and striking an acceptable balance between the imperatives to protect and understand the past and renew for the future.

3.3.4   Appropriate management information

A developer should ensure all relevant parties have clear project management information about key milestones and should insist on regular progress reports.

Reactive management of archaeological issues in the context of construction will always tend to increase archaeological risk, as unplanned changes to development programmes or foundation/construction design can be expensive.

3.3.5   Programming

The formal management of archaeological risk requires developers to adopt a risk management process before a planning application is formulated and submitted (Figure 3.1). Developers should understand the scale of any anticipated archaeological issue at a site before purchase.

Once development objectives have been established, assessing and evaluating a site and then designing and procuring evaluation and mitigation works takes time to plan and implement. Additionally there are important constraints that affect programming that the developer needs to take into account. For example, access for surveys may be delayed by crops, current land-use or tenancy agreements.

Checklist: laying the foundations for successful archaeological risk management

Much of the advice in this guide is general. However it is important that those involved in planning and carrying out property development in the UK understand how archaeology may best interact with their own schemes:

◆ understand the types of archaeological site and range of features that may occur (Sections 2.1 and 2.2)

◆ understand the range of non-intrusive and intrusive techniques that archaeologists may use to assess and evaluate archaeological remains, and how these help to identify and model archaeological risk (Section 2.3)

◆ understand what planning policy, statute and regulatory authorities will consider when deciding how to treat archaeological remains – especially the presumption in planning policy that favours the preservation of important archaeological remains *in situ* (Sections 2.3 and 2.5)

◆ understand the key roles of archaeological consultant, contractor and curator – the latter being the advisors and officers in government departments and agencies responsible for regulation (Section 2.4)

◆ recognise that archaeology is a fact of development and seek specialist archaeological advice at the earliest possible opportunity. If there is an archaeology issue, establish an integrated design team including specialist archaeological expertise, establish effective, face to face communications, factor in an appropriate window for dealing with archaeology and insist upon regular progress reports against agreed milestones (Section 3.3).

3.3.6   Insurance

Cost over-runs may be a significant problem for developers. They may be caused by:

◆ unforeseen discoveries leading to unforeseen requirements by the planning authority

◆ bad weather

Archaeology and development

- changes in the construction programme affecting access for archaeology
- poor advice from the appointed archaeologist
- oversight of the design team.

Although it is not common, it may be possible to insure against some types of cost over-run or delay, including against the risk of unforeseen archaeological discoveries causing delays, costs and even permanent loss of site value. The developer's archaeological advisor may comment on whether insurance is advisable and can brief the broker/underwriter on the developer's behalf.

Insurable risks: unexpected discoveries.

Delay costs – additional costs incurred in relation to the delayed completion of the development, which the insured is legally liable to pay. This can be the most significant unexpected cost to the developer and may include additional interest payments.

Additional archaeological costs - incurred in undertaking a scheme of archaeological work, including fieldwork, post-excavation work and preparation of results to an agreed standard for publication, as required by the planning authority or other statutory or curatorial organisation.

Cancellation costs – incurred as a result of the necessary cancellation of all or part of a project because of revocation of planning consent, or the designation of unexpectedly discovered remains as a Scheduled Ancient Monument.

Redesign costs – incurred as a result of a requirement to revise the layout or constructional details of a project to ensure the preservation of unexpectedly discovered archaeological remains.

Loss of profit – the nature of the profit would vary according to the insured's business but would include loss of rent.

Loss of value – in extreme circumstances an unexpected discovery might mean a loss of space or even a whole storey leading to reduced market value on the development.

(source: Robinson, 2002)

Obtaining insurance

Specialist advice from an experienced broker/underwriter is essential to agree appropriate terms.

Before any quotation for insurance can be given, an independent risk survey by the underwriter's archaeological consultant is usually required. The consultant's fee, commonly between £500 and £2000, has to be paid in advance and is non-refundable.

Underwriters' minimum premium for this class of business has been reported to be c£5000.

(source: Robinson, 2002)

---

4   Archaeology in the development process

This chapter summarises key elements of both the archaeology and development processes. It focuses on archaeological risk assessment and management and the contractual relationships between developers and archaeologists, with illustrations of good practice.

This guidance should be treated as flexible, as the interface between the various stages of archaeology and development projects is not fixed and each project may differ.

Case study 4.1 provides a good practice example of the entire process of integrating archaeology into a development programme, from the developer's perspective.

Case study 4.1   *30 Gresham Street, London*

Background

This Land Securities redevelopment site, about an acre (2.5 ha) in size, comprised several late 19th century and later buildings most of which had basements. The planning application included a desk-based assessment prepared by MoLAS that incorporated data from trial pits dug on-site, and from archaeological excavations on the adjacent redeveloped Guildhall Library site. The assessment concluded that Roman deposits potentially existed across about 70 per cent of the site.

The proposal was to leave archaeological remains *in situ* on the south side of the site. However, the closure of two small streets, Mumford Court and Russia Court, gave an opportunity to investigate better-preserved archaeology in areas that had not been previously developed.

Outcome

In the period leading up to planning approval, bids were invited from archaeological units with a proven track record of performance, credibility with the Corporation of London and the capability to carry out the work. A joint venture of two archaeological contractors (MoLAS and AOC Archaeology Group) won the tender. Land Securities was keen to spread the risk and resources given the size of the project and the joint venture provided greater reassurance of resources to Land Securities.

Land Securities worked closely with the archaeologists and the demolition and enabling works contractor (John F Hunt) to scope out the activities and sequence required both to access the important layers of archaeology and also to enable the demolition of existing buildings before archaeology could start. Where buildings had concrete framed structures the archaeology could proceed either before or in parallel with demolition progressing above so that the programme for these activities could be optimised.

Land Securities' project quantity surveyor, Gardiner and Theobald had a prominent role in facilitating the bids for both demolition and archaeology by quantifying the overburden that had to be removed by the enabling contractor and the possible quantities of archaeology earmarked for investigation and agreed with the local authority. In addition the quantity surveyor also agreed the scope of attendances required by the archaeological contractors provided by the enabling contractor. This rigorous approach was important for establishing accurate price and programming purposes, and also gave a basis for controlling costs and for pricing variations in work scope not anticipated at bid stage.

The enabling works also included temporary basement support piles and general reduction of levels following the archaeological investigations, pile probing and removal of obstructions and the laying of a piling mat across the site. This work was carried out to ensure that the ground risks had been dealt with before a building contract was placed. This strategy was extremely effective and assisted in delivering the work within programme and budget.

The relationships between Land Securities, John F Hunt, MoLAS-AOC and the Corporation of London established early on strengthened as the works progressed. The archaeological activities were filmed over their duration by Time Team and televised on Channel 4.

> **Lessons learned**
>
> ◆ early involvement of all parties involved in the processes including an appropriate archaeological contractor with a proven track record and an established relationship with the planning authority
>
> ◆ develop a procurement strategy that best manages and contains risks within an enabling contract and where possible avoid including archaeological investigations in the building contract
>
> ◆ rigorously scope out the works, interfaces, logistics and attendance requirements. A project quantity surveyor can quantify the overburden and the archaeological layers to be investigated. These figures can be incorporated into the bid documents
>
> ◆ where possible, employ enabling/demolition contractors who have experience in working with archaeological units on site investigations.
>
> *(source: Land Securities)*

4.1   FEASIBILITY, DUE DILIGENCE AND PRE-PLANNING STAGE

Fundamental to controlling the cost and programme of archaeological work is the early identification and assessment of archaeological hazards and risks.

4.1.1   When? As part of an initial feasibility study

◆ it is in the developer's own interests to include archaeology in the due diligence and research into a site's development potential

◆ ideally archaeology should be addressed as part of an initial feasibility study

◆ PPG 16 (Section B, paras 19–20) support this approach, advising that the developer should first consult the relevant local authority curator and Historic Environment Record for advance warning about a potential archaeological sensitivity. Secondly they should consider commissioning archaeological assessment by an appropriately qualified professional. As already noted, costs will rise in proportion to how late in the development and planning process archaeology is adequately assessed

◆ environmental due diligence (EDD) is an increasingly important part of any land or business acquisition, although research by KPMG (2004) has indicated that EDD sometimes misses material issues through insufficient depth and breadth in scoping. An initial site appraisal aims to address this

◆ developers are encouraged to treat archaeology as a material issue (Case study 4.3) and include an early due diligence test as the first step in a fully integrated risk management process leading from land assembly plans through to completion of the development.

> **Key advice: preliminary risk assessment**
>
> It is recommended that developers include heritage and archaeology in their due diligence studies and carry out an initial archaeological site appraisal as part of their land assembly process.

4.1.2   How? Scoping potential archaeological risk

♦   it is good practice to consider involving archaeologists in risk workshops and preliminary design meetings

♦   there are many occasions where the lack of early archaeological advice (on foundation design, basement location, landscaping works etc) from an archaeologically unacceptable scheme submitted for planning approval has resulted in substantial wasted expenditure.

4.1.3   What is the deliverable? An initial site appraisal

♦   an initial site appraisal involves developing an initial conceptual site model from high level desk study sources and establishing potentially unacceptable risks and constraints. It should be seen as an essential step for a developer during initial enquiries, to enable an informed decision about land purchase, development options and potentially significant constraints

♦   based on available information an initial site appraisal can grade the significance of a risk and its probability of occurring

♦   early advice can also be sought from statutory bodies to make use of detailed knowledge about particular sites that may be held by planning archaeologists. This may be informal advice, or it may be possible for the planning authority to formally advise whether any further archaeological work is required, or whether a desk-based assessment will be required to provide sufficient information for an informed decision. In some cases it may be immediately apparent that evaluation or mitigation works will be required. A sample risk assessment form is illustrated in Figure 4.1.

ISA risk assessment rating	High	Medium	Low
Archaeological risk		✓	
Probability		✓	
Historic buildings risk			✓
Probability		✓	

Probability		Risk	
Low:	unlikely to occur during the lifetime of the project	Low:	unlikely to affect asset value, design, project cost or programme
Medium:	can be expected to occur	Medium:	unlikely to affect asset value, may constrain design options. Likely to affect project cost and programme
High:	almost certain to occur	High:	potential to affect asset value/constrain design and have significant implications for cost and programme

Figure 4.1   *Example of an initial site appraisal risk assessment form (courtesy Scott Wilson Ltd)*

- potential cost estimates: although difficult to establish with any certainty at this early stage, developers should expect their advisors to estimate potential archaeological costs as part of an initial risk appraisal. Figures are likely to be broad brush. The initial site appraisal should be accompanied by a cost forecast for input to the developer's risk register. It is common to provide a cost range and likelihood rating, providing minimum and maximum cost estimates. This should take into account the size of the site, and quantity and complexity of surviving deposits, the site's geographic and topographic position (including access and logistical issues), previous land-uses and known archaeological information

- an archaeological entry in a project risk register (Figure 4.2) should outline possible minimum and maximum costs and likelihood of unforeseeable mitigation and post-excavation costs to arise. Actual sums, where entered, should be based on the professional judgement of the archaeological consultant/contractor given the site conditions, previous examples in similar conditions and knowledge of mitigation costs for particular activities

- cost estimates should be accompanied by a list of assumptions about archaeological remains and how they may be viewed, to illustrate the decision making process. This should include issues such as rarity value of the remains

- programme assumptions should be included taking into account both time (duration of investigation) and sequence. The potential impacts of archaeology on overall project programme are of particular importance, and the project team should identify key programme sequence issues at the earliest opportunity.

No	Owner	Item/hazard	Likelihood of hazard occuring (%)	Minimum (£k)	Likely (£k)	Maximum (£k)
ENa06	C	Conflicts with design or other mitigation strategies (redesign)	40	5	40	250
ENa07	C	Planning refusal	5	100	500	1000
ENa11	C	Unexpected discoveries	50	500	2000	4000

Figure 4.2   *Example of a project risk register entry for archaeology on a large development project (courtesy Scott Wilson Ltd)*

4.1.4   Why? Advantages to the developer

- if initial advice indicates that archaeology may be a significant cost on development, land purchase price might be negotiated on the basis of these projections

- alternatively, the seller might be asked to quantify the archaeological issues themselves before a sale is agreed (for example by arranging for their own archaeological desk-based assessment of the site, see Case study 4.3)

- at any stage of the project archaeologists can negotiate with the statutory or local planning authority on the developer's behalf

- broad brush cost estimates based on professional expertise can be included at an early stage

- even in the early stages of a project, archaeology can play a role in the dissemination of information (positive image of development) and community engagement.

Case study 4.2   *A1 road widening, North Yorkshire*

Background

In 2003, the £245m A1 widening works were being monitored under a watching brief by Oxford Archaeology.

Outcome

Work in one part of the route was halted by the discovery of a rare Iron Age chariot burial and skeleton (Figure 4.3). The find was hugely important and declared a find of national significance.

The emergency excavations were funded by the Highways Agency. Additional archaeological project costs were in the region of £250 000, including cost of off-site conservation work.

Lessons learned

◆ unexpected finds are a potential risk to development

◆ the risk of unexpected archaeological discoveries may never be entirely eliminated, although they can be reduced and managed by due diligence procedures.

Figure 4.3

The Ferrybridge Iron Age chariot burial (courtesy OA)

(source: Highways Agency)

Case study 4.3   *Land purchase price reduction*

Background

A housing association was interested in purchasing archaeologically sensitive land near Abingdon, Oxfordshire, from the Vale of the White Horse District Council.

Outcome

The housing association was able to negotiate a reduction in the purchase price of the land to cover the cost of archaeological investigations. However, these costs could only be quantified because the council had carried out an initial assessment in advance.

Lesson learned

◆ given sufficient due diligence, archaeological costs may sometimes be offset against land purchase price.

(source: IFA, 1998)

Archaeology and development

4.2 PLANNING APPLICATION STAGE

Initial site appraisals are confidential to the developer and design team. However, when applying for planning permission a developer will need to submit information about likely archaeological remains and the proposed approach to any archaeological issues. Depending on the archaeological remains, the planning authority can request a formal desk-based assessment report or Environmental Statement, or a report on specified site investigation works, such as observation of geotechnical works or pre-determination evaluation.

4.2.1 When? The statutory body or local planning authority will normally indicate their requirement, following preliminary consultation by the developer

♦ developers are urged to take specialist professional archaeological advice before applying for planning permission in cases where archaeology may be an issue. The checklist on early risk assessment gives an indication of what archaeological information developers should provide to the planning authorities, or risk having the application refused.

> **Key guidance: pre-determination**
>
> Pre-determination refers to the work conducted in advance of a planning application to collect enough information on the site to allow for an informed decision to be made by the LPA. Methods include desk-based assessment, intrusive evaluation, geophysics, field survey and other methods. Pre-determination investigations should be undertaken before the planning application is submitted, ideally as early as possible in the appraisal stage, as the results of the work may influence the final development.

♦ if archaeology is an issue (as established during early consultation), the planning authority may require the developer to submit a desk-based assessment in support of the planning application

♦ in some cases, where there is significant potential for important archaeological remains that will be affected by development, the authority may require the developer to carry out additional assessment work, perhaps including site investigation, before submitting a planning application

♦ the developer's archaeological advisor should establish early on the likely view of the planning authority and negotiate accordingly as to the level of detail they will require to determine a planning application.

4.2.2 How? Establish planning requirements and refine potential archaeological risks

♦ the planning authority may issue a brief for the work it requires to determine a planning application (eg a brief for a desk-based assessment)

♦ the developer or agent should appoint a specialist archaeological consultant or contractor to carry out this work

♦ the planning authority will require information in a specified report format, to enable it to reach an informed decision on the appropriate treatment of any archaeological remains. This includes all available information to permit a quantitative and qualitative assessment of the archaeological remains that still survive on the site such as documentary information and data from relevant fieldwork on or near the site, and details of how the prospective development may affect the remains

- the planning authority may also request a discussion of options to mitigate any impact on archaeological remains, although mitigation is usually the decision of the local planning/archaeology officer or curator

- these archaeological reports, although produced for the developer to submit to the planning authority to support the application, are an important step in refining a site's risk rating and likely financial impacts. This is a qualitative exercise that will use all available relevant information (including previous or completed surveys). The aim is to define zones of risk on the site, discounting the need for further assessment in some areas, while focusing the risk management process on specific areas where archaeological remains are likely to exist. At this stage it is important:

  - to involve the development team, to establish how and where design may affect archaeology and vice versa

  - for the development team to identify any programme and financial outcomes associated with land access constraints (such as ecological, contamination, current land-use values, crops and financial compensation issues) that may arise from further surveys

  - to establish what consents and/or consultation may be required with statutory bodies or third parties

- gaining planning permission does not mitigate the risk of archaeological remains affecting development plans and construction programming.

Where archaeological remains are suspected the development team should use the desk-based assessment stage to formulate responses to potential archaeological risks. Every effort should be made to refine the qualitative and quantitative assessment of archaeological remains long before starting on site, and to identify appropriate windows for archaeological work in development programmes even at this early stage.

Figure 4.4 illustrates the relationship between level of risk assessment and eventual mitigation (remediation) costs. The more quantitative information that can be gained from a site, the more focused and precise the understanding of the mitigation scope, programme impacts and financial impact. Quantitative risk assessment is appropriate to control risks to development plans and the developer's profit margins.

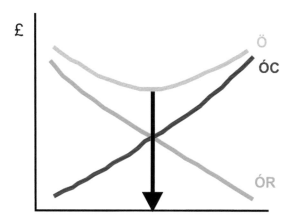

ÖC = cost of assessment (including investigation)
ÖR = remediation cost
Ö = sum of all costs

Figure 4.4   *Risk assessment financial cost levels (Newzeye, 2006)*

Key guidance: Defra advice on quantitative risk assessment

Generic quantitative risk assessment (Defra Tier 2) involves non-intrusive and field walking, secondary site investigation surveys (ie monitoring by archaeologists of site investigations carried out by others such as engineers) to establish the presence/absence of archaeological remains and to assign a likely archaeological significance rating. For example:

◆ archaeological monitoring of geotechnical site investigation or other non-archaeological investigative work

◆ geophysical surveys

◆ remote sensing surveys (aerial photography and Lidar, satellite)

◆ surface artefact surveys etc.

Detailed quantitative risk assessment (Defra Tier 3) involves comprehensive site investigation to establish a detailed subsurface deposit model to fully quantify remediation costs and further drive design to avoid areas of significant risk. This level of detail can be gained from:

◆ trial pit and trench surveys

◆ coring, borehole and auger surveys etc.

(source: Department for Environment Food and Rural Affairs)

Checklist: early risk assessment

◆ successful archaeology risk management starts at land assembly stage

◆ if archaeological risk is fully quantified mitigation programmes are more likely to succeed without surprises and be most cost effective

◆ professional advisors (consultants or contractors) should be employed to act as negotiators with statutory authorities and as the employer's agent to specify surveys and mitigation works (WSI's) and may supervise archaeological contractors to manage archaeological risks throughout the process

◆ good integration between the client's development team, planning team and archaeological advisor is a key success factor

◆ inadequate or an absence of previous risk assessment is a common theme in unforeseen events (Case study 4.2)

◆ make sure archaeology is included in any risk workshops and on risk registers

◆ there are high risk burial environments, such as waterlogged waterfront sites (Section 2.2) that increase the need for detailed quantitative risk assessments

◆ unforeseen changes can be managed successfully to limit effect of commercial/financial impacts (Case study 5.7)

◆ archaeological costs versus design change costs should be subject to a cost benefit exercise

◆ developers may be responsible for high off-site costs for analysis and conservation but can seek public partners for exceptionally important finds (Case study 5.12)

◆ asset values for property resale can be affected if archaeology is retained *in situ* in the ground and this should be taken into account in cost benefit analysis

◆ even a full and diligent risk assessment process cannot rule out unplanned costs or barriers to development (Case study 4.4), but good risk management during project construction will reduce commercial/financial impacts (Case study 5.11).

Background

In 2004, a 4 ha site was purchased by a client for residential development and an archaeological consultant was appointed. It was known that part of the site was probably the location of a medieval manor house. There were no statutory designations and outline planning permission was granted with condition that before finalisation of the detailed design an archaeological evaluation be undertaken and a written scheme of investigation (WSI) submitted to the local authority for approval.

An initial site appraisal highlighted an elevated risk within the area of the former manor house. An evaluation trial trench survey (detailed quantitative risk assessment) was later undertaken to establish the nature and extent of buried remains in the high risk zone. This identified that masonry and other remains survived below the topsoil at a relatively shallow level over an extensive area. However the quality of preservation was not exceptional.

As required by the planning condition, consultation was then undertaken with the statutory authorities with the aim of agreeing a mitigation strategy for the remains before construction. This was expected to consider many options including excavating the remains in advance of construction or preserving them within the site.

Outcome

The county archaeologist made an application to English Heritage to recommend designating the site a Scheduled Monument. The process of scheduling is complex and can take several months to conclude. More significantly, should the site be scheduled, any construction works would require new consents and possibly even limit the zone of potential redevelopment to an unacceptable level, affecting the commercial value of the purchased site.

At the request of the local authority English Heritage (EH) visited the site (Figure 4.5) and considered that the remains were probably not suitable quality for schedule. However, they indicated that they would need to undertake their own detailed assessment before a decision could be reached. Prompted by this response, the conservation officer for the county council took the decision to extend an adjacent conservation area to include the area of archaeological significance. The move provided further risk to the project programme and design detail because new constraints were introduced requiring the developer to seek conservation area consents for the new build.

In response to the risk of scheduling, the archaeological consultant and the client developed a new foundation design to preserve the archaeological remains *in situ* and the detailed design addressed the conservation area issues. These were agreed with the county archaeologist and an in-principle agreement with the local planning authority was made, pending the EH decision on the site.

After a six-month wait while the progress of the project was delayed and subject to additional design costs EH finally decided in favour of advising DCMS to schedule the site.

Figure 4.5   The county archaeologist and English Heritage inspect archaeological works at the Manor House (courtesy Scott Wilson Ltd)

Lessons learned

The process of evaluating archaeological remains beneath a site may be complex, and the process of ensuring they are protected may be both time-consuming and costly. Unforeseeable risks may sometimes occur. Risk factors to be considered include:

- the absence of an appeal process for either extension of conservation areas or scheduling of archaeological remains
- unplanned costs for redesign to avoid archaeological remains and achieve preservation *in situ*
- unplanned delay while EH and LPA consider changes to the site's designations
- unplanned costs associated with future need to obtain consents
- commercial impacts on value of land and limitations on extent and type of development for current use and future sale of site.

(source: Scott Wilson Ltd)

What are the deliverables?

(i) **The desk-based assessment report, or relevant chapter in an environmental statement**

If the site is archaeologically sensitive, the minimum likely requirement on the part of the planning authority will be a desk-based assessment report.

A desk-based assessment (DBA) addresses the known and potential archaeological resource of a site or area (see IFA, 2001a). The work should be undertaken by a specialist archaeological consultant or contractor. Depending on the availability of design detail, DBAs may include a section considering the potential archaeological impact of the development proposal.

Some projects (Section 4.3.3) may require formal Environmental Impact Assessment (EIA). Although the methodology for EIA varies (for example, there are specific requirements for scoping, baseline surveys and mitigation), the principles of DBAs also apply to EIA.

What does DBA require? A report based on the collation of existing written and graphic information, to identify the likely character, extent and relative quality of the actual or potential archaeological resource. The archaeologist should agree the aims and methods with the planning authority in advance.

Archaeological issues are easily identified if more information is available. So it is helpful to obtain information on below-ground deposits at an early stage of the project: archaeological involvement in/observation of any geotechnical boreholes, engineering trial pits, geophysical or other archaeological surveys etc is always useful.

What is it for? The purpose of a DBA is to source and collate information to establish the potential for archaeological features and the presence, significance and quality of known sites of historic interest. The work includes a search of local Sites and Monument Records, local study library archives, aerial photographs, historic maps and estate records, and a site visit. The assessment allows the archaeologist to produce a list of sites, with a description, potential, approximate date, references, and further recommendations. The DBA helps to prepare an informed strategy for any further work.

Terminology and implications of archaeological importance

DBAs for submission to the planning authorities or statutory bodies will usually classify archaeological remains as follows:

◆ nationally important sites, whether scheduled or not, represent remains that are rare at the national level and should be preserved *in situ* in line with government policy. Scheduled (Ancient) Monuments (Section 2.5) are nationally important by definition. Although a rare occurrence, should a site of potential national importance be discovered in the course of development or archaeological work, it may be considered for scheduling (for example, the Roman bathhouse complex at Shadwell, London (Case study 5.11), or the Newport ship (Case study 5.12). Developers are expected to use appropriate design measures, or to avoid impacts, to preserve nationally important archaeological remains *in situ* (Section 4.4)

◆ regionally or locally important sites that contain archaeological remains of regional or local importance will also be considered by the local planning authorities in determining a planning application. If the significance of the archaeological remains is not sufficient to outweigh other material considerations, including the need for the development, the proposed development is likely to proceed subject to approving an archaeological mitigation strategy. Planning authorities will need to satisfy themselves that the developer has made appropriate and satisfactory arrangements for the preservation *in situ* or excavation and recording of the archaeological remains, and publication of the results (ie preservation by record or replacement by record).

◆ many sites may be found to have no archaeological importance following a desk-based assessment.

Who will use it? The DBA is used by the applicant/developer, the archaeological designer and the whole design team, as the report may inform the design of their development. Most importantly it will be considered by the planning archaeologist who will use it to assess the impact of the proposed development and what further archaeological measures are necessary (eg targeted evaluation, mitigation or a full programme of excavation). DBAs are also a useful source of information on the geological, historical and archaeological background for members of any archaeological contractor's team involved in on-site work.

(ii) Monitoring geotechnical works

The developer should consider the benefits of commissioning the archaeologist to monitor any geotechnical investigations that form part of the site appraisal. Geotechnical works do not need formal approval if the site is not scheduled at the time of the works. Such works can provide a valuable opportunity for archaeologists to observe and record below-ground conditions: they can reduce the need for further archaeological site investigation or help to target further work and can provide a greater measure of certainty for the developer at an early stage of their project.

Who undertakes the work? The monitoring is usually undertaken by an archaeological contractor who should produce a report that can be provided to support a planning application.

What will the monitoring require? The archaeologists will observe the excavation of geotechnical test pits and make additional records regarding any archaeological deposits that may be present. The geotechnical team should liaise with the archaeological contractor to ensure that both sets of records are consistent.

Case study 4.5   *Assessing evidence for modern disturbance*

Background

A desk-based assessment at the site was commissioned in advance of an extension to a business centre at Newburn. The site was found to have been occupied by a large Scots army during the Battle of Newburn Ford on 28 August 1640. There were no other recorded archaeological sites in the area and it was decided, in consultation with the archaeology officer for the LPA to undertake a review of previous disturbance at the site.

Outcome

It was clear from the topography that the site had been terraced in the past. Analysis of the historic map sequence showed that the Newburn watercourse had been raised on an embankment at some point between 1859 and 1920 to accommodate railway sidings. It was apparent that the most likely source for the material for construction of this embankment would be the proposed development site.

The results of historical geotechnical investigations on the site were carefully analysed which indicated recent made-ground across the majority of the site to a depth of between c1.5 m and 4.0 m. With reference to historic mapping, the expected level for the superficial geology of glacial till was found only to be present in a limited area at the eastern edge of the site.

To confirm the conclusions of the modern disturbance review, additional geotechnical test pits within the proposed development site were monitored by an archaeologist. This established that layers of demolition material and levelling deposits were present down to the solid sandstone geology, precluding the survival of any archaeological remains. No further archaeological works were required in advance of construction.

Lessons learned

♦ it is important to thoroughly assess the source and extent of any previous modern disturbance

♦ it may be possible to use existing records to identify areas within the site where modern disturbance precludes the potential for archaeological remains

♦ initial findings can be tested through the monitoring of geotechnical test pitting or focused trial trenches.

(source: Scott Wilson Ltd)

Archaeology and development

(iii) Pre-determination archaeological field evaluation

In addition to DBA, to enable accurate and confident decision making, the planning authority may require a limited programme of non-intrusive and/or intrusive fieldwork to determine the presence or absence of archaeological features and finds. If such features are present this field evaluation will define their character, extent and relative quality so that their worth may be assessed in a local, regional and national context.

Archaeological field evaluation (IFA, 2001c) should also consider the likely impact of the proposed development on archaeological remains, and consider options to mitigate such impacts. Evaluation reports may or may not contain recommendations for further work. So it is common practice for developers to request advice from their appointed archaeologist on the likely expectations for further work.

The aims and methods for each evaluation, from project planning through to completion of a report and deposition of an archive, should be agreed in advance with the planning authority. The work should be governed by a written scheme of investigation (WSI) or a project design approved by the planning authority against which performance may be measured.

Case study 4.6   *Pre-determination evaluation*

Background

On a large urban site, a field evaluation (trial trenching) was carried out in the basements of the standing buildings before the planning application was submitted.

Lessons learned

The advantages can be summarised:

♦ the necessity of a break in the development program between demolition and construction (for archaeological works) was substantially reduced

♦ there was sufficient time for the results of the evaluation to be incorporated into the design

♦ there was sufficient time for the archaeological consultant or contractor to negotiate an acceptable mitigation strategy with the local curator.

(source: MoLAS)

Where significant remains may exist, it is good practice for field evaluation to be carried out before applying for planning permission (Case study 4.6). So both the statutory/planning authorities and the developer have more information for the next stage of the project. If statutory/planning authorities are not provided with sufficient information to determine a planning application, it may be refused. Early evaluation benefits the developer by reducing risk.

The four steps involved in field evaluation are as follows:

1   The planning authority issues a brief for archaeological evaluation.

2   The developer appoints a specialist archaeological consultant or contractor to carry out this work.

3   The archaeologist supplies a specification (WSI or method statement) to be approved by the planning authority.

4   The archaeologist carries out the evaluation:

   a   field evaluation may often involve non-intrusive methods, such as geophysical survey – a method of detecting below-ground features and anomalies using techniques such as resistivity, magnetometry and ground penetrating radar

(GPR). A specialist is required to both use the field equipment and interpret the data. The type of technique used and its overall effectiveness are very dependent on soil and geological conditions within the site area.

Geophysics as an assessment tool

Background

A rapid response was needed by a developer to discharge an archaeological planning condition attached to a very large rural site. The timescale from commissioning to discharge was constrained by the developer's programme of works and needed to be eight weeks.

Outcome

The local planning authority (LPA) requested a desk-based assessment followed by trial trench evaluation. This would not have been achievable within the required timetable. So it was agreed with the LPA that a geophysical survey be designed and commissioned to facilitate a targeted trial trench evaluation.

Within two weeks of receiving an intention to proceed a detailed geophysical survey was designed, approved by the LPA and carried out. This identified a limited number of features of potential archaeological significance at the site. In consultation with the LPA, a targeted trial trench evaluation focusing on features identified by the geophysical survey was designed and commissioned.

The results of the trial trench evaluation indicated that there was no need for further archaeological work before or during construction.

Through this quick and robust approach the discharge of the archaeological planning condition was secured within seven weeks of initial commission.

Lesson learned

♦ geophysical survey can be an important stage in the evaluation of a site and the design of intrusive archaeological works

♦ LPAs may be open to negotiation in reference to their archaeological assessment briefs.

(source: Scott Wilson Ltd)

Detailed site evaluation involves intrusive investigations such as the excavation of trial trenches or test pits. The amount of work required is usually estimated as a percentage of the total area of interest. The number and size of trenches or test pits excavated will depend on the type of archaeological remains anticipated and the sample size agreed with the planning authority. Test pits range from pits on the most restricted urban sites, to larger trenches on sites with unconstrained access, such as large rural sites. Trenches are commonly excavated using a JCB or tracked excavator and (toothless) ditching bucket, with the overburden (topsoil and modern material such as tarmac) removed under archaeological supervision down to the first archaeological horizon or geological (natural) deposits. Archaeologists should clean the sides and base of the trenches to expose and record the depositional sequence.

If archaeological remains are found they should be cleaned and inspected by the planning authority archaeology officer. Some archaeological features may be sampled (for example a 50 per cent sample of the infill of a pit may be taken for analysis), and it is not uncommon for the planning archaeologist to require additional trenching if that will add greater certainty to the site interpretation. The developer should ensure any additional trenching is clearly defined and agreed before the work starts.

How long will it take? Ground conditions and archaeological deposits are too variable to give any specific indications, although the issue should be discussed and targets agreed in advance of any field evaluation. In general, greenfield sites with little overburden will be quicker to machine strip, clean, sample and record than deeply stratified, urban, or waterlogged sites, which can be much more complex.

Archaeology and development

The archaeologist will prepare an evaluation report for the developer to submit in support of the planning application.

The archaeologist may also provide separate, confidential advice to the developer on the possible requirements for further work and the need to scope future archaeological risks accordingly.

The report should be produced within an agreed period following the fieldwork. It will describe the findings (it will serve as a publicly accessible record of the remains) and will also offer an archaeological interpretation of what has been found. A section on recommendations should be included, as the basis for later discussions and negotiations between the development team and the planning archaeologist.

Typical recommendations are:

◆ no further archaeological measures are considered necessary

◆ archaeological remains were found, which may be significant. A detailed scheme of archaeological investigation should be agreed to ensure that the remains are appropriately investigated and a durable record created

◆ significant archaeological remains were found and the development has been revised so as to minimise or avoid impact

◆ archaeological remains of potential national or international significance were found. It may be recommended that the proposed scheme should not proceed, or that a mitigation scheme will need to be designed that allows for the archaeological remains to be preserved *in situ*.

In some cases the planning authority may defer the need for archaeological evaluation to a later, post-determination evaluation stage, and grant planning permission with a planning condition for archaeological evaluation. Although this is not normally good practice in some cases it is the only option, for example in urban developments where early access may not be possible. It is in the developer's interest to complete evaluations as early as possible to avoid uncertainty later in the development programme. In this case, evaluation work should be carried out soon after outline development design stage, to support the development team in targeting archaeological fieldwork on areas of likely development impact.

Key guidance: negotiation of evaluation works

The appointed archaeological consultant or contractor should negotiate on the developer's behalf with the planning authority, to agree a firm strategy for evaluating the potential and significance of archaeological remains.

Pre-determination evaluation can be time consuming and costly. The appointed archaeologist should draw on comparable examples to support negotiations for an appropriate level of sampling, commensurate with the likely importance and potential of the remains.

4.2.4 Why? Advantages to the developer

For risk management the developer should be clear about the nature and extent of surviving archaeological remains, and about potential archaeological issues.

A desk-based assessment enables the full development team to consider in more detail possible archaeological risks at a stage when design can provide solutions.

Physical site investigations test the assumptions made at desk-based assessment stage. For example, by commissioning an archaeologist to observe and record geotechnical or other groundworks, the developer can maximise information and reduce costs.

Pre-determination evaluation can be costly, especially as investment is still at risk, and a developer may try to negotiate for evaluation after planning permission is obtained. However, post-determination evaluation only increases the potential impact of any unexpected significant remains on cost and programme.

Archaeology is, by definition, about discovery so the greater the investment in assessment and evaluation before planning, the greater the certainty for the developer (Figure 4.5).

Checklist: required information for planning applications

Applications for planning permission should:

◆ demonstrate due regard to national legislation

◆ demonstrate due regard to national planning guidance

◆ demonstrate due regard for archaeology in accordance with the policies in the local authority's development plan or the core strategies and area action plans in the authority's local development framework

◆ be supported with a desk-based assessment report prepared by a suitable archaeological specialist, including an assessment of the archaeological impact (Section 4.3.3) of the proposed scheme

◆ incorporate results from any other intrusive or non-intrusive investigations into actual or nearby site conditions (eg geotechnical reports, ground radar surveys)

◆ involve the local authority archaeology officer in discussions

◆ be supported if appropriate by an archaeological evaluation report

◆ include sufficient detail about the proposed scheme (particularly impacts ie building locations, basements, foundation type and layout, areas of likely groundworks, present ground or slab levels on-site and proposed levels and extent of new ground reduction), including detailed scale plans and sectional drawings. These can be discussed with and approved by the local authority archaeology officer before submission.

On the basis of the assessment of this information by the local authority archaeology officer, permission may be granted without conditions, refused, or granted subject to conditions.

4.3   PLANNING PERMISSION AND CONTROLS

Planning controls over development are discussed in Sections 2.5.5 to 2.5.6. Most planning authorities publish supplementary planning guidelines explaining how archaeology will fit into the planning process. Figure 4.6 is an illustration of the combined archaeology and planning process from a local authority perspective.

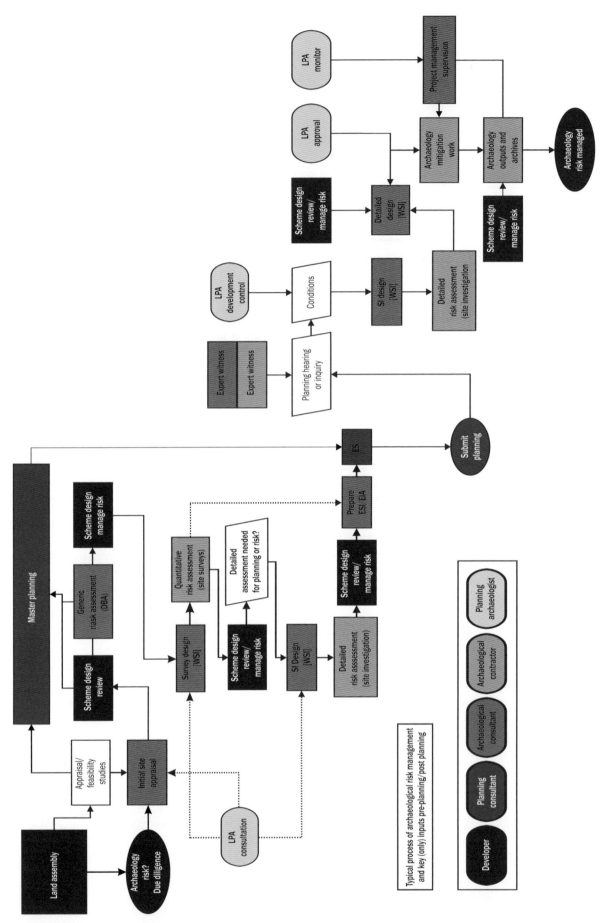

Figure 4.6   *Flow chart illustrating archaeology within the planning process (from Corporation of London, 2004)*

The granting of planning permission may be subject to the developer's adherence to certain conditions.

Key guidance: archaeology and planning applications

◆ presence of archaeological remains, even on non-designated sites, will be regarded as a material consideration in the planning process and should be adequately assessed, as is the case with other environmental constraints (eg contamination, wildlife)

◆ archaeological impact should form part of the consideration for all developments requiring planning permission

◆ it is presumed in European and UK planning policy and guidance that important archaeological remains shall be physically preserved, whether or not they are protected in law by designation

◆ any potential damage to important archaeological remains by development or construction is viewed as a significant environmental impact. Any such potential impact requires mitigation measures be sought

◆ mitigation measures include the concept of the preservation of archaeological remains:

  ❖ *in situ* ie by design measures, removing or reducing the potential impact

  ❖ by record ie by adequate excavation and recording of the threatened archaeology and by the analysis of the results. Preservation by record, or replacement by record, is only complete once the results of archaeological investigation are stored in the requisite archive and made available to the public

◆ the person or organisation developing the site should provide accurate and timely archaeological advice to the statutory authorities in relation to planning applications and pay for all necessary costs involved in determining the presence and condition of remains, archaeological fieldwork and later research and publication following the established environmental principle that the polluter pays (cf EU Directive, 2004).

◆ nationally important archaeology should be preserved *in situ*.

4.3.1   Archaeological planning conditions

Archaeological planning conditions are designed to protect archaeology, and developers are obliged to:

◆ fence/protect areas of archaeological interest

◆ arrange for an archaeological watching brief during construction

◆ agree and implement an archaeological mitigation strategy according to an agreed written scheme of investigation (WSI).

The latter may include further archaeological field investigation, excavation and post excavation (Sections 4.5 to 4.7), or measures to preserve archaeological remains *in situ* by design measures (Section 4.4), or a range of approaches for different areas of a development/locations along a linear scheme. These various measures are sometimes referred to as a scheme of works.

4.3.2   Section 106 Agreements

Section 106 of the Town and Country Planning Act 1990 allows a local planning authority to enter into a legally-binding agreement or planning obligation, with a land developer over a related issue. The obligation is sometimes referred to as a Section 106 agreement (Case study 4.8). These agreements should be entered into by any parties that hold an interest in the land in question.

Archaeology and development

Background

The Bath SouthGate redevelopment is a large (c3.24 ha) and complex project by Multi Development and Morley Fund Management immediately south of the Roman and medieval walled town. Mitigation of the development's impact on archaeological remains is being achieved by a Section 106 agreement.

A detailed WSI was prepared by the client's archaeological contractor. This document forms an appendix to the Section 106 Agreement and is legally binding on the developer, the principal contractor and the archaeological contractor.

Outcome

The LPA's archaeology officer and the client's archaeologist monitor the implementation of the S106 Agreement, by a series of regular meetings and site visits. The document sets out a detailed framework for further evaluation and a range of options for excavation depending on the results, as well as the research framework guiding the archaeological work and the methods and techniques to be employed. This arrangement ensures both that archaeological elements of the historic environment are adequately preserved by record, or *in situ*, and that the client and principal contractor are afforded a degree of certainty as to the scale, nature, costs and duration of the archaeological work.

Lessons learned

A Section 106 Agreement is a legal document ensuring that all parties are held to the agreed mitigation scheme.

(source: MoLAS)

4.3.3   Environmental Impact Assessment requirements

For certain types of development formal Environmental Impact Assessment (EIA) may be necessary. Where it is required, the developer should provide an Environmental Statement (ES) setting out the information specified in Schedule 3 of the regulations about the site and the likely significant effects of the proposed development on the environment. This should include information relating to any significant effects on material assets and the cultural heritage, such as archaeological features and other human artefacts, and the measures envisaged to avoid, reduce or remedy adverse effects.

Where development requiring EIA affects the site of a Scheduled Monument or listed building, the national heritage body should be consulted on the submitted Environmental Statement and they may be able to provide additional information for the statement.

EIAs should provide a high level of detail on the effects of a proposed development on all material assets and the cultural heritage. This will include:

♦ the development's effects on Scheduled Monuments and their settings
♦ other archaeological sites
♦ the potential for the disturbance of presently unknown archaeological remains
♦ listed buildings
♦ historic gardens and designed landscapes
♦ conservation areas and their settings.

The assessment work should be undertaken by a qualified archaeologist.

Further information about the EIA procedures may be found in DOE Circular 15/88 and the booklet *Environmental assessment – a guide to the procedures* (HMSO, 2000).

4.4 DETAILED DESIGN STAGE

This section covers issues relevant to the design of archaeology works for development plans. It describes key objectives, how archaeological design aligns with typical project work stages (RIBA, DRMB etc), what development factors affect archaeological design, and what developers should expect from good design documents.

4.4.1 Archaeological design for development

Archaeological design refers to the approach taken by the design consultant to preparing briefs and specifications for any required evaluation and mitigation works. It should result in several deliverables described above and summarised in Figure 4.7. These include project strategy documents, written schemes of investigation and specifications for surveys, site investigations and excavation or protection works. Design deliverables will also include post-excavation designs that define and justify the scope of the reporting and dissemination stage. Good archaeological design is also a fundamental part of archaeological risk management.

Design deliverables	ISA	Desk-based assessment (DBA)	WSI for surveys	WSI for site investigations	Supporting documents for Planning	Detailed design for construction (WSI)	Post-excavation (updated WSI/project design)
Typical works	Data review, Report	Documentary research, Site visit, Report	Monitoring geotech, Geophysics, Field walking	Trial pits, Trial trenches	ES Chapter, Technical appendix, Drawings	Excavation, Preservation *in situ*	Assessment, Analysis, Publication and dissemination options, archives
Sources/content	High level, existing knowledge	Extensive, new data from site specific surveys or additional documentary searches	Scope, Specification, Tender docs, Cost/estimate, Outline programme	Scope, Specification, Tender docs, Cost/estimate, Outline programme	ISA, DBA, Surveys	Scope, Specification, Tender docs, Cost/estimate, Outline programme	Updated research aims and objectives, costs, programme
Level of analysis	Generic/area based, largely predictive	Qualitative, detailed for site and surrounds	Quantitive site specific	Quantitive site specific	Qualitative and quantitive statement of significance	Quantifiable and measured, specific to site	Final analysis for publication
Reporting	Broad statement of potential	Detailed factual statement and scope for WSI, Interpretative site deposit model and detailed plans, Outline costs and scope of mitigation	WSI with scope, specification and deliverables	WSI with scope, specification and deliverables	Specialist chapter and drawings	Detailed specification, timing and order of work explained, Cost and programme	Post-excavation assessment report, Final project analysis report, Publication materials and research archive
Highways Agency equivalent	Preliminary assessment	Rapid assessment	Detailed assessment	Detailed assessment	ES	Tender for construction	Post fieldwork
RIBA stage	A	B	C	C	D	E–G	K–L
Network Rail Standards	GRIP 2	GRIP 3	GRIP 4	GRIP 4	GRIP 4	GRIP5	6–8

Figure 4.7   *Summary table showing typical archaeology design deliverables aligned with building and infrastructure development work stages*

Figure 4.7 describes the archaeological design deliverables for a typical development programme, what works are covered, sources and content, level of analysis and reporting, and how they may align with the wider design process such as those outlined for building projects and infrastructure works. These are iterative stages with each design deliverable informing the other and it is important to avoid programme conflicts by allowing sufficient time to scope, implement, complete and review each stage.

Archaeological design should be guided by the research significance of archaeological remains that are affected. Where archaeological excavation is required, the objective is not merely to create an inventory of archaeological deposits but to ensure that meaningful information is provided for research purposes. Without a research agenda archaeology is merely data collection.

Key objectives: archaeology and development design

◆ meaningful research quality of information gained from mitigation works
◆ integration with development design objectives, costs and programme
◆ integration with other below-ground issues
◆ integration with planning guidance and standards
◆ achieve a balanced response to development impacts
◆ identify planning, cost and programme risks early.

Key guidance: design drivers

Archaeological professionals and the design team should:

◆ focus on the current condition of archaeological deposits on the site rather than their historic condition or their potential
◆ understand previous impacts (eg from extractive industries or previous construction that may have damaged or removed archaeology)
◆ ensure that survey and evaluation data meets quality standards
◆ zone the site to indicate relative significance levels – as well as areas where development should be straightforward and areas where careful design choices need to be made
◆ examine likely impacts from proposed development
◆ understand relevant policy and good practice
◆ understand ways in which the design of the archaeological response can impact (either favourably or adversely) on the development programme
◆ recognise the ultimate research dividend and value of the new knowledge that should result from the archaeological works.

4.4.2   Development factors that affect archaeological design

Archaeology is the study of physical remains of the past. Good archaeological design depends on development teams understanding the importance of addressing archaeological issues at the right stage in the development process and being aware of the purpose of archaeological works. The purpose is not to undertake archaeological investigation for its own sake, but to provide meaningful research outputs or research dividend – knowledge and understanding – to mitigate the damage or loss of the resource.

Typical development design stages enable a robust decision making process to be implemented transparently, and help the development team to manage risk. Timing is critical, as integrating archaeological design at the right time in the process is an important success factor. Fitting archaeology around scheme design that is already fixed may mean missing the opportunity to avoid or minimise development impact on archaeological remains, or indeed to design a cost-effective programme of investigation.

Mitigation design is dependent on good quality surveys. Many archaeological survey options depend on site conditions. Rural sites with arable crops will constrain surveys, and urban and brownfield sites may require demolition and site clearance to be completed before survey. The right time is as soon as practicable. Delaying archaeological design can seriously affect programmes.

Managing detailed design changes is essential. For example, introducing geo-engineering solutions for soft ground may be a sustainable alternative to dig and replace, but is difficult to address in the archaeological design. Inclusion of additional land at a late stage in the design process may require the scope of any surveys to be expanded so it is not always possible to extrapolate results from neighbouring land parcels.

It is important that archaeology design documents focus on impacts of a particular development and assess the impact (or outcome) on the archaeology. Can an alternative layout or methodology avoid disturbing archaeological remains? Can protection measures be taken to minimise impacts of a temporary nature? Methods include low ground pressure plant and protective fill layers with geo-membranes (Case study 4.9).

While impacts from earthworks, structures and building foundations are often taken into account some of the key construction issues that impact on archaeological remains may be less obvious and need careful consideration, such as:

- impacts from essential temporary works. Provide protective measures where possible

- impacts from non-essential temporary works (eg soil stores and haul roads with consequent compression, plant impacts). Move to less sensitive locations if possible

- visual impacts such as impacts on the setting of monuments, buildings and the wider historic landscape may need a careful design response

- impact from ground improvement techniques on buried archaeology. Deep soil mixing, wick drains and vertical concrete columns may seriously damage significant archaeology and prevent preservation *in situ*. Invasive evaluation and mitigation works may be required ahead of the ground improvement, and if time allows pre-loading earthworks may be a better alternative if compression issues are shown to be minimal.

- changes to ground water levels and quality.

4.4.3 Achieving good design

Good design requires teams to be well integrated and relevant information is effectively assembled and exchanged. Figure 4.7 shows a typical range of interfaces between the design archaeologist and other members of the development team and third parties. The design archaeologist should make effective contributions to design review meetings and this should be encouraged in the early stages of the development plan.

4.4.4   Preservation *in situ*

Government planning guidance (Section 2.5.5) emphasises the need for developers to attempt to mitigate disturbance to archaeological sites, preferably by preserving them *in situ*.

In general all below-ground works (foundations, basements, drains and services, vent shafts, pipelines, tunnels etc) and landscaping should be designed to reduce damage to archaeological remains to an acceptable level. Indirect impacts such as changes to long-term burial environments (eg desiccation or compression of remains) will also need to be considered. Research into the long-term effects of re-burial is slowly advancing (see further guidance). However curators are still wary of preservation *in situ* as a mitigation design where precedents are lacking. Specialist geotechnical advice may be required to demonstrate the validity of a preservation design (Case study 5.16).

Developers should balance cost, archaeological significance and long-term preservation issues when adopting a preservation *in situ* design. The definition of an acceptable level of disturbance will vary from site to site, depending on the nature, preservation and significance of the archaeological remains, the presence or otherwise of any designated assets and the views of the individual curator. Where preservation *in situ* is not a viable option, full excavation may be required (Case study 4.9). What is essential is for a design archaeologist to ensure that the design team's mitigation option can be fully justified before negotiating approvals from LPA or statutory curators.

Further guidance: preservation *in situ*

Advice on preservation *in situ* is available from heritage bodies, for example, English Heritage regional science advisors (see Appendix A1 for contact details).

Published research and guidance on aspects of preservation *in situ* schemes is now available:

◆ *Reuse of foundations* (Butcher *et al*, 2006)

◆ *Piling* (English Heritage, 2007b)

◆ *Mitigation practice* (Davis *et al*, 2004)

◆ *Research and case studies* (Corfield *et al*, 1998 and Nixon (ed), 2004)

◆ *Reuse of foundations* (Chapman *et al*, 2007).

Case study 4.9   *Preservation in practice – modelling compression*

Background

An option for preservation *in situ* was considered to protect nationally important Roman and Anglo-Saxon buildings on the site of the Ebbsfleet International Station for the Channel Tunnel Rail Link in Kent. The site lay on the alignment of a high railway embankment. The height of the embankment was up to 11 m so it was important to consider potential compression impacts. These were modelled by combining archaeological and geotechnical expertise. A settlement model was produced by combining archaeological evaluation and geotechnical site investigation data.

Outcome

The study indicated that the likely vertical and horizontal distortions to the buildings would be unacceptable. This was due to variable superficial geology that underlay the archaeology. A boundary between two geologies was found to run diagonally across the area and the model predicted that the slight difference in strength in these soils, combined with the significant weight of the embankment would result in significant distortion (up to 400 mm) leading to the break up of the buildings remains. Discussions were held with English Heritage and the local authority and a decision to fully excavate the remains was made. Due to the cost of providing an alternative (structural) preservation method, and the poor condition of some of the archaeology, it was agreed that the research dividend from full excavation would outweigh the case for preservation *in situ*.

Lessons learned

◆ preservation *in situ* schemes require careful specialist review and analysis. Curators will expect detailed empirical evidence to be provided indicating possible long-term effects

◆ statutory regulators can be pragmatic where physical preservation *in situ* for nationally important archaeological remains is not achievable, providing the proposed development is essential and an acceptable mitigation strategy in place.

(source: Union Railways Ltd/CTRL Ltd)

4.4.5 Preservation for display

In exceptional cases, archaeological remains may be found that are substantial and stable enough to be suitable for incorporation within the finished scheme, for example to provide historic depth or a focal point for a scheme or neighbourhood. This is rarely possible to predict in advance, so is an area where some flexibility of design is necessary. Examples include excavated structures preserved *in situ* as part of the mitigation scheme, but also those consolidated, protected and displayed to the public (Case study 5.17) or (usually less significant) structures that can be dismantled or lifted for display *ex situ* at a more suitable location within the finished scheme. Where preserved or excavated archaeological remains are not suitable for permanent display design, temporary or permanent exhibitions and artwork may illustrate the remains (for example Case study 5.16).

A good practice guide on the preservation and display of archaeological remains within urban developments has been produced by the European Commission (2006). Together with various case studies, the guide is available on the APPEAR website: <http://in-situ.be/A_pres_overview.html>.

4.4.6 Master planning

The creative design team potentially has the most influence in the successful management of archaeological issues when consulting the design archaeologist at the early options stage.

It is good practice to:

♦ ensure that assessment for archaeology and heritage in general is completed sufficiently early to influence the layout and style of the development

♦ seek early guidance from the design archaeologist on key constraints and/or appropriate responses in sensitive locations

♦ ask the design team to look for opportunities to add heritage value to a development by incorporating historic interest into the development brief.

4.4.7 Design teams

In the design stages the input of geotechnical, structural and civil engineers will ensure that archaeological surveys and mitigation design are responsive to the needs and constraints of the project.

It is good practice to:

♦ ensure the design team integrates archaeological investigation with other site investigations and enabling works where possible (an archaeologist should observe site investigation works for primary data on archaeological potential, or discuss expanding the investigation to include archaeological interventions or taking additional samples)

♦ supply site investigation results to the design archaeologist as soon as possible. Request clear information on archaeological constraints and risk for use in key engineering design decisions, such as selecting alignments for infrastructure developments

♦ consider impact on archaeology when designing earthworks, structures and ground improvements and provide specialist input to the archaeological design response and mitigation

◆ consider programme and cost issues for archaeology when planning enabling works and construction works

◆ take specialist advice and include archaeology on the risk register

◆ give early warning to the design archaeologist of any significant design changes.

4.4.8 Construction teams

Archaeological contractors and the construction teams need to work closely and proactively to ensure a professional approach to archaeological work and that there is understanding between the different teams.

It is good practice to:

◆ ensure that drawings are available to the construction team that clearly indicate the extent and scope of archaeology mitigation works, constraints or exclusion zones and required support and attendances

◆ always ensure that archaeological contractors provide a comprehensive method statement and health and safety plan or risk assessment

◆ hold weekly programme and progress meetings and insist on written reports from the archaeologist

◆ brief the archaeology contractor on the contract risks and ensure early warning is given of potential timing issues

◆ for complex projects, request that the archaeologist provide tool box talks to site staff to explain the works and what is needed from site teams to support work

◆ use temporary boundary fencing and notices to direct construction teams on presence of archaeology works on site and control access to excavations

◆ ensure that a procedure is in place identifying key personnel and actions needed in the event of unexpected discoveries on site. Have alternative working plans prepared to deal with site constraints and site sharing with archaeological contractors

◆ ensure that archaeological contractors are fully inducted and working to the same health and safety rules and welfare requirements as all other teams

◆ ensure that archaeological contractors are fully briefed on utility risks and environmental constraints/consents especially where they are entering land first.

4.4.9 Statutory regulator

The role of the various regulators is described in detail above (see also Section 2.4). As a third party to the development team, regulators can have a significant impact on the progress of archaeological mitigation works. The regulators are responsible for monitoring the progress and results of archaeological works and will negotiate from the position that all reasonable and practical measures should be taken to preserve archaeology *in situ* or that a full and detailed investigation be completed to a high standard (below and Section 2.5).

In the UK the regulatory bodies are encouraged to provide a service advice role as opposed to one focused only on supervision and official authorisation. The regulator is a source of advice at all stages of a development project and proactive management of the relationship should be encouraged.

It is good practice to:

◆ ensure the design archaeologist undertakes early discussions with the local authority or heritage agency and establishes a good working relationship, keeping the regulators informed and supportive of the scheme

◆ be aware that regulators have prepared a range of design guidance to encourage sensitive development solutions

◆ seek regulators' advice on all aspects of the process including regional research priorities, community interests and public outreach opportunities, and post-excavation publication and museum and archives

◆ be aware that negotiation is an important factor in how planning policy and legal consents are agreed and enforced. Archaeological remains and the historic environment are tangible assets. However, the importance of the assets to the communities that value them varies widely and there is reasonable scope for negotiating where that value is best met and resources are directed

◆ in large or complex projects, involve regulators in early design reviews to ensure they gain an understanding of the project details and objectives

◆ encourage regulators to discuss opportunities for historic environment enhancements that could arise from the project. These may become valuable assets to the project

◆ ensure that adequate programme time for approval and agreement of design documents and consents applications is built in

◆ ensure that adequate programme time on site is allowed for regulators to inspect and agree completion of archaeological works on site.

Key guidance: negotiation with regulators

Key questions which may need to be resolved by negotiation include:

1　What is the interpretation resulting from the archaeological assessment and evaluation?

2　What is the significance and research potential of any archaeological remains?

3　What will be the impact of the development on the archaeological remains and how will that affect their research value?

4　Which areas will require full excavation?

5　Which areas should be preserved *in situ*?

6　How will preservation be achieved?

7　What construction operations will need to be monitored under an archaeological watching brief?

8　Can the design be modified (for example altering basements, foundation types and layouts or land raising) or methodologies designed in to reduce the area of disturbance, and the amount of archaeological excavation required?

9　Are elements of the design unacceptable (for example piling through a cemetery site)?

10 What is the curator's attitude to the time constraints of the developer's programme?

Development teams should supply curators with sufficient information to allow them to be satisfied that the mitigation brief and planning conditions will be met. This will usually involve the submission and agreement of a detailed method statement or WSI.

Successful negotiation will establish and agree the limits of what is required, reasonable, practical and mutually acceptable to all parties.

Archaeology and development

4.5   DEMOLITION AND ENABLING WORKS STAGE

Archaeological work often takes place during pre-construction phases. Depending on site access and safety archaeology may take place before demolition or even during it, or during preliminary site works. On major schemes especially those in historic towns with deep archaeological deposits, enabling works are often required to ensure the structural integrity of ground, buildings or perimeter walls not only for construction but also for the archaeology itself.

Impacts from enabling works on archaeological deposits will be a concern for local authority and statutory curators and should be carefully considered during the design phase of a project (Section 4.4). As with other aspects of development design, curators should be satisfied that affects on archaeology from enabling works have been reduced as much as possible.

Enabling works may directly or indirectly affect archaeological remains. Affects include:

◆   removal of existing foundations

◆   probing for and removal of other obstructions

◆   ground reduction carried out in association with retaining walls: secant/diaphragm walls, temporary supports, tie-backs (ground anchors), tower crane bases, service diversions etc.

Topsoil stripping or ground reduction to form construction compounds etc may also disturb archaeological remains.

Other impacts include:

◆   compression from haul roads or ramps

◆   contamination of archaeological deposits during the installation of grout curtains

◆   dewatering operations (that alter the soil conditions and may have allowed the preservation of important waterlogged archaeological deposits).

Curators will expect archaeological impacts from enabling works to be reduced as much as possible by design measures, and for unavoidable impacts to be mitigated by archaeological watching brief or excavation, as appropriate.

Enabling works may be carried out ahead of construction, as part of a demolition contract, but more usually as an immediate prelude to the main construction phase. Many of the processes described in more detail in Section 4.7 apply equally if archaeological fieldwork is carried out during the enabling works phase. In many situations it is desirable to conduct the enabling works and any necessary archaeological evaluation and excavation ahead of the main construction (Case study 4.10). Careful consideration of programme will be necessary, but there are obvious advantages in dealing with archaeological risk at an early stage of the process before main construction starts. Note that the advantages of carrying out archaeological excavation works during an enabling works phase that is ahead of construction will need to be weighed against the need to provide plant and labour etc for these works, as well as archaeological attendances before the site has been resourced for the construction phase.

Background

The East London Line is a major railway scheme, running north to south from Dalston, through East London, beneath the Thames and linking to the south London rail network via Rotherhithe and New Cross Gate. It consists of improvements to the present infrastructure, using existing tunnels and viaducts, together with new bridges, stations and other construction. The archaeologist carried out desk-based studies and project design work for the Strategic Rail Authority and Transport for London, targeting the localised areas where archaeological mitigation may be necessary. This has included surveying disused 19th century railway viaducts. Other sites identified include medieval Holywell Priory.

Outcome

Archaeological assessment (field evaluation and some excavation) was integrated into the enabling and geotechnical works programme, ahead of main construction, reducing risk to the main construction programme.

Lesson learned

♦ combining archaeological evaluation and excavation with enabling works ahead of construction reduces programme risk.

(source: MoLAS)

4.6   CONSTRUCTION – MAIN WORKS STAGE

4.6.1   Programme

Because of the understandable desire of developers/clients/contractors to keep development programmes as short as possible, often the main site-based phase of archaeological works takes place within the main construction phase of a project. This is rarely good practice, as potential risks from unforeseeable discoveries can have a serious impact on construction programmes (see Case study 27 and Section 5.12). Wherever possible archaeological excavation works should be programmed well in advance (either physically in the case of a linear project, or chronologically in the case of an excavation arranged to take place pre- or post-demolition) of the main construction phase to minimise the risk of disruption to construction programmes. Monitoring of preservation *in situ* schemes of necessity should take place during construction operations.

If archaeology takes place alongside construction, it is important to devise a programme and method of working that keeps archaeological and construction areas separate. Consideration of a phased programme of archaeological work and construction (see for example Case study 5.6) should be possible on all but the smallest sites. On projects where there are particular pressures, special measures may be designed into the project (Case study 4.11).

Background

No. 1 Poultry was a large site in the heart of the Roman and medieval City of London, in an area known for important archaeology and waterlogged conditions leading to excellent preservation of organic remains.

Outcome

Following desk-based assessment, and evaluation in the form of monitoring contractor's bore-holes and evaluation trenching, sufficient archaeological information was available to allow the developer (Altstadtbau Ltd), the archaeological contractor (MoLAS) and the curators (Corporation of London and English Heritage) to design a top down construction sequence for the ground level slab and basements to allow the necessary large-scale archaeological excavation to take place within the strict engineering and timetabling constraints of the construction programme.

Following an archaeological watching brief on necessary operations (mostly piling) the perimeter walls and ground floor slab of the new building were constructed. The structure was designed to allow deep archaeological excavation to then proceed beneath this slab while construction of the superstructure continued above it (Figure 4.8). The ground floor slab formed a physical barrier between archaeologists and overhead construction work.

Lesson learned

♦ imaginative design can achieve cost effective solutions, such as reduced programme duration.

Figure 4.8

Excavation in progress beneath the ground floor slab of No. 1 Poultry, City of London (courtesy MoLAS)

(source: MoLAS)

4.6.2   Legal, planning and contractual obligations

All parties should be fully aware of any legal consents, planning conditions or other agreements relating to archaeology. Difficulties can arise on site if those who were probably not party to early discussions do not know all the details of the mitigation scheme.

Site teams should establish in advance whether archaeological risk has been considered during the project planning stages, and ask for copies of all relevant documentation. Developers should ensure that the requirement to provide access and attendances to archaeologists is defined in the contract documents. Equally the form of contract is essential to ensure that archaeological risk transfer is properly managed (Section 4.8.3).

Where contractors on site are unfamiliar with working alongside archaeologists, training should be considered (see CIRIA C650 *Environmental good practice on site*, 2005). For each site, specific information should be given to all personnel regarding archaeological and construction programmes and areas of work, to ensure both archaeological and construction staff are aware of each others' operations and objectives.

4.6.3   Attendances

In most situations, the developer, the principal contractor or a named sub-contractor is contractually responsible for providing attendances to the archaeological contractor during on-site evaluation or excavation works. Attendances can add considerably to the cost of dealing with archaeology, and resource requirements should be worked out in advance of fieldwork. On site, a specific contractor's agent should be designated to implement agreed attendances.

Archaeology and development

Checklist: attendances

Attendances can vary depending on the size of projects and the nature of the archaeological remains. Attendances may be subject to negotiation and special requirements, but a typical list for a large excavation would include:

◆ mechanical excavator(s), plant and operators (number, size and type appropriate to site conditions eg breakers, toothed buckets, large toothless ditching buckets. Kangos or hammers with compressors to remove small obstructions during the course of the excavation), all to be used for topsoil stripping, removal of overburden, breaking out and removal of modern material

◆ space for spoil storage or provision for safe removal from the site

◆ means of removing spoil generated during excavation (mechanical excavator(s), hoists, conveyors and labourers as appropriate)

◆ a temporary roof or portable horticultural-type tunnels (of translucent plastic to allow daylight through) available to cover archaeological deposits and permit archaeological work, if necessary, during bad weather. Roofing needs to be equipped with suitable means (gutters etc) of keeping the waterflow out of/away from the areas of archaeological work. Although such roofing may be expensive, it can prevent considerable delays in periods of prolonged bad weather and should be considered where important and/or complex sites have to be excavated over winter in situations where little flexibility can be built into the programme

◆ safe access routes installed before the excavation and maintained throughout the period of the excavation

◆ necessary shoring installed in accordance with safety regulations and maintained throughout the occupancy of the area in question

◆ gas monitoring equipment when depth, restricted space or concerns over air quality require it

◆ safety guard-rails and suitable access points into the site and areas of excavation, away from any site traffic and machinery

◆ ladders into all areas of excavation when the excavated depth requires such access

◆ duckboards or other suitable system for safe spoil removal and general site traffic

◆ if necessary, tungsten halogen lamps (500W minimum) with 110-volt transformer, adequate cabling and power supply

◆ if groundwater is encountered adequate pumps, with generating equipment, if needed

◆ a suitable security system to operate overnight, at weekends and during holidays. Normally this means adequate hoarding and locks, but a guard may sometimes be required

◆ accommodation for the site staff during the site clearance and excavation (a lockable mess area with lighting, electrical points (if possible), heating, water supply, chairs, benches and tables, a lockable office area with lighting, appropriate power supply, heating, chairs, tables or desks, shelf units, lockable filing cabinet

◆ male and female toilets/changing rooms (with hot and cold water where possible)

◆ lockable storage areas on-site for tools and equipment, finds and samples.

Some sites will also require:

◆ on-site processing facilities, with water supply, silt trap for environmental processing, racking/shelving to facilitate drying (on-site processing can, in some cases, significantly reduce overall archaeological programmes)

◆ separate lockable processing huts for finds and environmental archaeologists with overhead lighting, two double power points (if possible), water supply, drainage away from the excavation areas, work surfaces and slatted wooden shelving

◆ use of a photographic tower, or safe access to adjacent structures, to make a photographic record.

4.6.4   Archaeological works on site during construction

It is often best to deal with archaeological issues (including excavation) in advance of the start of the main construction phase (Section 4.5). It is good practice and in the developer/client/main contractor's interests that all field evaluation work (Section 4.2.5) is completed and an agreed mitigation strategy (if required) is in place before construction/groundworks start.

In practice, there are many situations, particularly the requirement for the development to proceed along the shortest critical path, logistical demands or aspects of the mitigation strategy, that result in on-site archaeological works taking place during the construction phase. Such works may consist of archaeological excavation, archaeological watching brief on construction operations, or watching brief on the implementation of preservation *in situ* schemes.

The size of an archaeological team will vary according to the project. Most on-site archaeological work will be undertaken on a full-time basis, for an agreed duration, although watching briefs may be staffed on a part-time basis, with archaeologists attending particular construction operations by arrangement with the site manager.

All archaeological areas, including areas where the mitigation strategy calls for preservation *in situ*, should be clearly delimited and access to other site traffic and personnel carefully controlled. This is a legal requirement in the case of scheduled areas. Good communications (Section 4.6.5) will aid the smooth running of archaeological works during the construction phase and are essential if archaeologists and construction crews are to understand each others roles, programmes, methods of safe working etc.

Before agreed excavation areas are handed over to an archaeological contractor, and when completed areas are handed back to the construction team, it is good practice for there to be a meeting between the archaeological contractor and the health and safety officer, the main contractor's site manager and the client's representative. The purpose of such meetings is to ensure that site conditions are acceptable and safe, that contractual, planning conditions and legal obligations are carried out to the satisfaction of all parties.

Finally, certain below-ground construction operations tend to occur after archaeological excavation phases have finished, for example sewer headings. In some cases, these operations have archaeological implications that should not be overlooked by developer/clients, planners or archaeologists.

4.6.5 Management and communications

The key to good management of the archaeological process within a development project is the sharing of information and effective communication between all parties involved.

Effective channels of communication are essential. The developer should ensure that each member of the project team understands the required communication routes, authority levels and key issues (eg public relations, site access): these may be covered in a construction management plan.

4.6.6 Health and safety, CDM regulations

Archaeological investigations on site vary greatly. An investigation may involve nothing more hazardous than scraping away shallow soil accumulations of a few centimetres, or they may involve deep excavations that may collapse (whether made by hand or using machinery) or working on old masonry structures that may become unstable, ie similar to a civil engineering or building project. As soon as there is any significant risk to those carrying out the work, those in charge must give serious consideration to their duty of care for those involved and their responsibilities under relevant legislation. Management of the work, expert advice, insurance etc will need to be addressed and if you are not expert you must seek advice. Note that risks may come from many sources, including dormant spores etc. Expert advice should be sought on initial risk assessment before deciding how to proceed.

Archaeology and development

If the work is being carried out as part of a larger construction project (such as the construction of a new road or building) the site will be a construction workplace and it will come under the requirements of the Construction Design and Management Regulations (CDM) 2007 (CDM2007). The professional team involved (designers and contractors) will ensure that the client is aware of CDM2007 requirements. Assessment of risks by all involved will be necessary and those in control of the site should ensure that the work is carried out safely. Archaeologists will be required to co-operate and co-ordinate with others including (for all but the smallest projects) the CDM co-ordinator (appointed by the client) to advise and co-ordinate on health and safety matters, particularly during planning and designing and the principal contractor who is responsible for managing and co-ordinating the safe execution of work on site. Full details of CDM (including the wording of the legislation itself) are contained in HSE L144 *Managing health and safety in construction*. Further information can be found through the Health and Safety Executive (HSE) website <http://www.hse.gov.uk/>.

If the work is not part of a construction project, the legal position may be less clear. CDM2007 only applies to construction work as defined and a pure archaeological investigation is not included in the definition given. However, legal liability in the UK is widely drawn and the duty of care for the health, safety and welfare of others cannot be ignored. Whoever is managing the work will have legal liabilities. So it is recommended that unless the initial risk assessment demonstrates that there is no significant risk, the requirements of CDM2007 are met for the work. Note that the CDM2007 duties can also be carried out by any competent person on behalf of some or all of the parties.

Archaeological contractors are responsible for providing their employees with a safe and healthy working environment. The health and safety of the project team should be considered to be of the utmost importance. All archaeological contractors should have their own health and safety policies and their own designated health and safety officers or external specialist consultants. Current health and safety legislation and regulations should be treated as the basic minimum standard to be achieved on site.

Compliance with relevant health and safety legislation, regulations and codes of practice constitutes one of the key non-archaeological constraints on the design of archaeological excavations.

Archaeologists should carry out their own health and safety training of staff at induction, general and managerial levels, and should liaise with the principal contractor and/or attendance contractor to ensure that the approach to health and safety is harmonised on site.

Many archaeological excavations take place on brownfield sites that have been contaminated by generations of industrial use. If from previous uses there is reason to believe that the ground or adjacent buildings may be contaminated, the developer/client should make arrangements for and undertake pollution sampling and testing before archaeological work on site takes place.

The developer/principal contractor should provide all information on contamination and the location of live services before archaeological site works starts.

It is good practice for health and safety provisions to be included in legal agreements between developer/clients and archaeological contractors. Method statements and risk assessments should be exchanged between the attendance contractor and the archaeological contractor, and all site sub-contractors should be aware of the archaeological requirements.

An archaeological contractor's health and safety officer or consultant should visit a site regularly and provide written reports after each site visit. These reports should be copied to the site supervisors, archaeological project managers, and the health and safety officer of the main contractor and/or attendance contractor. Regular liaison between health and safety officers of archaeological and principal/attendance contractors throughout the periods of excavation will help to ensure safe working. Both should attend hand-over meetings at the start and end of archaeological fieldwork.

It is good practice that stand-down time resulting from excavation areas that become unsafe is not deducted from the archaeologist's time on site.

4.6.7 Press and public relations

It is good practice to inform the public of the progress and results of archaeological work on site. Archaeology has the potential to contribute in many ways, including generating favourable publicity for the scheme and the development team, and enhancing the sense of place for local groups and end-users.

Consideration should be given before site works begin, of how archaeology can be integrated into any publicity. Involving local schools, for example, can be an excellent way of including local children and their families. Failure to provide information or the uncontrolled release of publicity can be harmful – especially if a development is perceived as harmful to archaeological remains or other heritage assets.

Once archaeological mitigation work starts on site it may be appropriate to produce press releases, display boards or exhibitions to explain the findings, and advertise the support given by the developer. Many archaeological organisations employ press and or educational professionals in-house, or have links to museums that offer such services. Alternatively the archaeological team can contribute material to the developer's own public relations team for dissemination. Subject to security, health and safety and programme considerations, viewing galleries or conducted tours for interested parties, schools, or the media may be an option. Case studies 5.16 to 5.20 offer examples of the benefits of good practice.

On some sites, archaeological remains may be so important or valuable, or the development so sensitive, that it may be better to agree a public relations plan that delays the release of information until the archaeological site works or the development itself is finished (Case study 4.12).

Case study 4.12   *Managed publicity*

Background

During the excavation of Roman buildings on a large development site, the archaeological contractor discovered a hoard of 43 gold coins dating from the first and second centuries AD. The find was of considerable monetary value as well as archaeologically important. It was reported to the coroner to determine its possible status as treasure (Section 2.5.4).

Outcome

To avoid possible security problems on-site, and to satisfy the terms of the Treasure Act, a press release about the find was delayed until the archaeological excavation was completed.

Lesson learned

In certain situations it is important to manage information releases about archaeological discoveries. In this example legal and security concerns were addressed by delaying a press release, but the developer benefited from favourable publicity at a later stage.

(source: MoLAS)

Archaeology and development

4.6.8   Accidental discovery

If suspected archaeological objects or remains are found in the course of construction operations without an archaeologist on site, certain procedures should be followed.

Archaeological finds should not be further disturbed without specialist investigation and advice. Non-specialists should not attempt to lift objects, blocks of archaeological material, or structures out of the way of construction, and finds not already disturbed should be left *in situ*.

There are legal obligations to report all archaeological finds in Scotland, or all items classed as treasure in the rest of the UK, to the appropriate authorities (Section 2.5.4).

There are specific legal obligations if human remains are accidentally disturbed (Section 2.5.3).

All archaeological finds discovered during the course of non-archaeological works should be reported to the local planning authority archaeology officer or national heritage agency.

Good practice: accidental discovery

In the case of any accidental discovery of archaeological finds or human remains, it is good practice to:

◆ stop work in the area of the find
◆ leave the find *in situ* (ie keep it intact and undisturbed)
◆ control access to the area to unauthorised persons
◆ stop vehicle traffic over the area
◆ report the find to the site manager
◆ take specialist advice if appropriate
◆ report human remains, treasure and other archaeological finds to the appropriate statutory authority
◆ report the find to the appropriate LPA or other curator.

4.6.9   Security

Site security is a serious consideration on all development sites. Archaeological contractors engaged in works on site should be provided with secure, lockable, office and storage accommodation (Section 4.6.3).

The presence of archaeological remains on site can raise particular security issues. If the site is well publicised while work is still ongoing, or if it becomes known that valuable finds have been made, site managers may be advised to consider additional security measures to discourage unauthorised entry to the site. Security may range from mobile patrols to a permanent security office and even alarm systems.

4.7   POST-CONSTRUCTION, OFF-SITE PROCESSES

The developer's responsibility for archaeology does not end when the archaeological site work is complete. Off-site archaeological works are widely referred to as the post excavation stage of a project and involve laboratory work and detailed analysis and reporting of the findings.

This section provides a brief guide to the post-excavation stages of a project, to assist developers/clients in understanding their obligations, the specialised terms used by curators and contractors, and in negotiating the costs of off-site work. It also highlights areas where there may be benefits for developers/clients in promoting their involvement in such work.

The framework for the off-site stages of archaeological projects across the UK has been set out by English Heritage (2006a). Slight variations apply in Scotland (Historic Scotland, 1996a and b).

The basic processes are summarised in Figure 4.9. This represents current good practice and should apply to any site. Not all stages will apply in all cases, particularly if the actual archaeological results were less significant than predicted.

The process begins towards the end of fieldwork, when the archaeologist may either prepare a summary or interim report or other short statement to specify whether the findings require a post-excavation assessment (Section 4.7.3), or could move straight to archive preparation and deposition, with a summary means of dissemination (Section 4.7.5). This should be discussed and agreed with the client and relevant regulator.

Archaeology and development

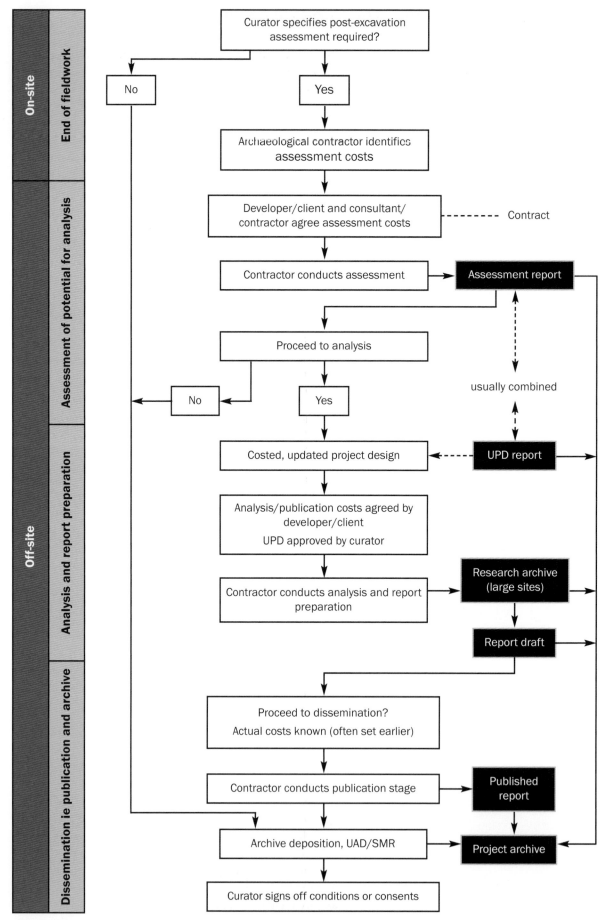

Flowchart labels:

On-site
End of fieldwork

Off-site
Assessment of potential for analysis
Analysis and report preparation
Dissemination ie publication and archive

Curator specifies post-excavation assessment required?

No

Yes

Archaeological contractor identifies assessment costs

Developer/client and consultant/ contractor agree assessment costs — — — — Contract

Contractor conducts assessment → Assessment report

Proceed to analysis

No

Yes

usually combined

Costed, updated project design ← — — — UPD report

Analysis/publication costs agreed by developer/client
UPD approved by curator

Contractor conducts analysis and report preparation → Research archive (large sites)

Report draft

Proceed to dissemination?
Actual costs known (often set earlier)

Contractor conducts publication stage → Published report

Archive deposition, UAD/SMR → Project archive

Curator signs off conditions or consents

Figure 4.9   *The stages of a post-excavation project (courtesy MoLAS after English Heritage, 1991)*

4.7.1   The role of post-excavation in discharging planning conditions

The artefacts, samples and data collected during fieldwork should be processed, conserved, collated, studied, recorded, archived and published to be of any benefit to the profession, the wider academic world, the public and future generations.

Developers should consider the possible impacts of post-excavation work on their costs and programme, as this stage represents a substantial element of any archaeological project. Post-excavation work should be managed as closely as on-site works.

It is good practice for planning authorities not to fully discharge an archaeological planning condition (Section 2.5.5) until after the production of a finished report and the deposition of the site archive. In practice, however, many curators will take the pragmatic approach of signing off conditions (so allowing the development to proceed) once they are satisfied that a funded program of works is in place that will lead to publication and archive deposition. In some cases a performance bond may be required to ensure that the terms of the condition are honoured.

Key issues: post-construction processes

◆ post excavation works can be time consuming. As a very approximate guide, a post-excavation programme will take 1.5 days for every day of field excavation

◆ post-excavation works can be expensive, often at least 50 per cent of the on-site archaeological costs

◆ the full cost of the post-excavation programme can only be accurately estimated on completion of the post-excavation assessment (Section 4.7.5)

◆ before fieldwork starts developers should enter into an agreement with an archaeologist to complete post excavation

◆ the extent of beneficial publicity that developer/clients obtain from their support of post-excavation work is likely to depend on the reports being produced and the chosen publication media.

4.7.2   Interim report

Although not covered by Figure 4.8, it is good and common practice, especially on larger projects to produce an interim report as soon as fieldwork is completed. Although no substitute for the detailed work that follows, interim reports (in digital, in-house printed, or externally published format, as appropriate) can be an excellent way of communicating the results of the developer's support of archaeology to the archaeological community, the public and the press.

4.7.3   Post-excavation assessment

Post-excavation assessment or assessment of potential for analysis should be conducted by an archaeologist "to evaluate the potential of the data-collection to contribute to archaeological knowledge and to identify the further study necessary. The complexity of the assessment phase and the amount of time required will vary" (English Heritage, 1991), and will depend on the nature of the archaeological remains. The archaeologist should produce a post-excavation assessment report, which should allow an informed decision to be made regarding the requirement for further analysis and publication. In practice, where it is clear that this further stage is required, the post excavation assessment report is usually combined with an updated project design that specifies the extent of analytical work required, as well as proposals for publication and archiving, and the work required to achieve these ends. The report should provide the basis for the negotiation and agreement of a costed programme of analysis and publication work (usually submitted separately by the contractor).

In Scotland, and Northern Ireland, a similar role is fulfilled by a data structure report (see for example Historic Scotland, 1996a and b).

The assessment stage is usually concerned with the collection of quantitative (for example processing environmental samples and dating the pottery) and qualitative data (for example checking site records, or selecting which sampled timbers should be sent for radiocarbon dating) and the consideration of how these relate to the research aims set out in initial project designs or wider regional or national research agendas. In the case of smaller, less significant sites, sometimes the work undertaken for assessment removes the need for a separate phase of analysis later.

Post-excavation assessment reports and updated project designs should be approved by the relevant curator. Discussion and negotiation may be necessary to reach a proposal for further work that is acceptable to all parties.

The process ends either with the submission of a brief site summary to the appropriate archaeological journal (in Scotland this summary should be part of the data structure report) and HER/SMR and, if required, a decision to proceed to analysis.

4.7.4 Analysis and report preparation

The contractor should carry out the analysis according to the costed programme of work agreed following the post-excavation assessment/data structure report. Curators are responsible for monitoring this process. The analysis phase ends with the production of an organised research archive, a draft report and a final decision and costing for the place and format of publication (or dissemination), if appropriate.

Often a simple report is all that is required, detailing the work carried out in the field and with a brief section on the finds. Some sites, however, might take years to fulfil the updated project design requirements. The more complex the archaeology on a site and the richer the artefacts and environmental material recovered, the more significant the post-excavation costs will be, as a proportion of the overall budget.

4.7.5 Dissemination (publication and archive)

The form and costs of publication vary widely depending on the nature of the project, the archaeological remains recorded and the wishes of curators and clients. This may range from an SMR entry, a digital record of fieldwork through the Online Access to the Index of Archaeological Investigations (or OASIS <http://ads.ahds.ac.uk/oasis> now England and Scotland only) a note in the fieldwork round-up section of an archaeological journal, a longer article in a journal, or a stand-alone book/monograph. In addition to any required academic reporting, developers/clients may find it advantageous to ask the archaeologist to produce shorter, more accessible and well illustrated reports or leaflets on the findings, for the purposes of publicity, public education etc.

Developers/clients are responsible for the costs of the publication programme. Publication grants from archaeological societies or heritage bodies are only rarely made available for developer-funded projects. Increasingly, web-based publication is being used as a means of publishing some or all of the results of a project. In some cases it may prove a cheaper option than traditional printed media, and can reach a wider more diverse audience.

All projects, even those where no analysis and/or publication takes place, should produce a stable and ordered site archive comprising site records, reports and artefacts (Brown, 2007).

The archive should be deposited with an appropriate archive or museum, for long-term storage and to guarantee public access. Developers/clients are responsible for the costs of preparing this archive and for the payment of a one-off storage grant to the archive receptor.

As yet there are no nationally agreed standards for archaeological digital archives. Advice and good practice guidance is available from the national heritage bodies, or from the intended receptors of such information (eg the Archaeology Data Service, <http://ads.ahds.ac.uk/>), but a digital archive will be needed by all projects commissioned by heritage bodies, or which involve large collections of primary and analytical digital data. Digital archives have been developed for several large commercial archaeological projects, including CTRL. As with traditional archives, there will be a charge for preparation and storage – the ADS estimate that an overhead of up to five per cent (and more usually one to three per cent) of the total archaeological budget would meet the costs of digital archiving.

It is good practice for archaeologists to agree publication and archiving costs with developers/contractors on completion of the analysis phase, as only then can they be stated accurately. In practice, these costs are sometimes agreed at earlier project stages, but with the risk that if funds are insufficient, the curator may still hold the developer/client responsible for completion.

Good practice: publishing the results and depositing a unified project archive

All archaeological projects should result in a single, professionally curated, ordered and accessible archive. Regardless of whether more than one archaeological contractor or developer has been involved (for example on different sites making up a larger scheme or different stages of work), developers and archaeologists are required to:

◆ prepare site records in a unified way (so related work is compatible and integrated)

◆ agree and commit to an appropriate level of publication

◆ ensure deposition in a suitable curated repository of a single archaeological archive.

These requirements are both a professional obligation for the archaeologist and an obligation on the part of the developer to fulfil a planning condition(s).

4.8 FORMS OF CONTRACT

This section deals with the main forms of contract commonly used to regulate business relations between developers, archaeological consultants and contractors.

A client should commission an archaeologist:

◆ to identify, assess and control archaeological risk

◆ to carry out the archaeological work that is needed to meet the requirements of national legislation and government policy

◆ to act on the client's behalf to ensure that the development project conforms to planning authority advice and that conditions are duly discharged.

4.8.1 Standard forms

A variety of standard forms are in use. The standard form of contract for archaeological work *Conditions of contract for archaeological investigation* (ICE, 2004a) was developed by the Institution of Civil Engineers in partnership with the Association of Consulting Engineers, the Civil Engineering Contractors Association and the Institute of Field Archaeologists.

Archaeology and development

> **ICE *Conditions of contract for archaeological investigation* (ICE, 2004a)**
>
> Suitable where:
>
> ◆ an employer (client body) wishes to appoint an archaeological contractor to perform an investigation under the supervision of a separately defined consultant
>
> ◆ the consultant is not party to the contract, but will be commissioned by the employer under a separate professional services agreement.
>
> **NEC 3 short contract or sub-contract <http://www.neccontract.co.uk/>**
>
> Suitable where:
>
> ◆ an employer (for example a design or planning consultant or contractor) wishes to appoint an archaeological contractor to perform an investigation on behalf of a client
>
> ◆ the client is not party to the contract.
>
> **JCT contracts and NEC main contracts <http://www.jctcontracts.com/>, <http://www.neccontract.co.uk/>**
>
> Archaeology investigations are often let as sub-contracts with JCT forms, or NEC or ECC main contract. So provision for suitable additional clauses may be appropriate to align construction contract with the specifics of archaeological investigation.

Two contract forms have been predominant in procuring archaeological services:

1   The simple professional services sub-consultant's agreement within which items of fixed price and time-based activities can be combined in a simple schedule of works.

2   A non-standard form of the lump-sum agreement that may often be based on a letter of appointment and perhaps a list of outline tasks to which an archaeological organisation provide a price (and their terms and conditions).

Professional service agreements can be an appropriate way of procuring consultants services or minor contract works that can be accurately costed.

A simple letter of appointment and short list of costed items and terms of appointment may be appropriate for some contracting tasks, but usually only where the scope is fixed, the value insignificant and the outcome easily predictable (for example monitoring of some geotechnical test pits).

Simple agreements are fine for low risk/low value works. However as risk and value increases, archaeological works need to be treated in similar ways to other services where formal contract forms (based on ICE or NEC) are used. These properly describe the roles, responsibilities, measurements and quantities, and who pays for what and when. A formal contract form provides a robust legally binding agreement where the risk share and method for administering the contract is fully understood and stated. This is to the benefit of all parties and certainly required in high risk situations such as watching briefs.

Before publication of the ICE's Conditions of contract for archaeological investigation, consultants and contractors would regularly use the long standing ICE *Conditions of contract for ground investigation* (ICE, 2003), which closely mirrors the needs of archaeology evaluation and mitigation works with some fine adjustments. Some may still find value in using this form. The ICE form requires an employer to separately appoint (or nominate) a consultant to administer the contract. In terms of good practice the consultant should be an archaeological specialist.

The NEC forms of contract, particularly the short form and sub-contract form, are used for procuring archaeological survey and mitigation works. These provide the client with the good level of control over costs and programme. There are multiple pricing options and ways to incentivise and share risks with the contractor. The NEC is a two-way contract in that it can be set up between any two parties. The NEC form is often used by archaeological consultants and design organisations that employ and supervise archaeological contractors on behalf of a client body.

The JCT's contracts were conceived to spearhead contract standardisation to reduce litigation and other legal costs within the development sector. Archaeology works can be let as sub-contract to any one of the numerous different contract forms, from the minor works contract to the major works contract.

4.8.2   Apportioning risk

Different contract forms in construction projects provide for varying risk balance between clients and contractors (Figure 4.10). The same applies to procuring archaeological works.

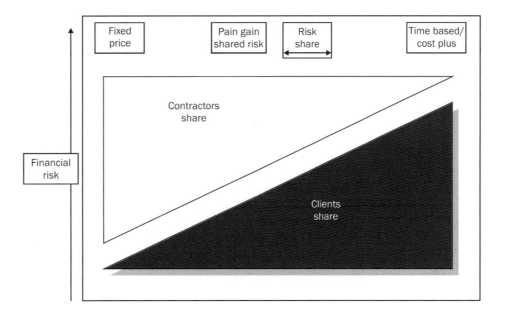

Figure 4.10   *Risk sharing between clients and contractors applies equally to archaeological works*

Archaeological works that are relatively easy to accurately quantify include surveys and site investigation evaluations. These are more likely to be tendered on a fixed price or lump sum basis, subject to variations managed through a bill of quantities and schedule of rates included in the contract.

Fixed-price contracts may not be guaranteed fixed price. Contaminated land consultants and contractors offer guaranteed fixed price remediation contracts to developers supported by insurance cover or other form of financial indemnity (such as company balance sheet). This is a full risk transfer for the client and appropriate to the potential level of risk posed by contaminated land remediation. It is unlikely that a developer will find archaeological organisations with sufficient financial resources to take on board this level of risk. However insurance arrangements may be available to developers to limit their exposure to cost overruns.

Archaeology and development

For more complex archaeological programmes and where a main or principal contractor is carrying the majority of the risk for the client, such as in design and build contracts, ECI, PPP and PFI projects, some form of shared risk is likely to be appropriate.

4.8.3 Advice for developers where archaeological issues are to be transferred to a main or principal contractor

Archaeology can regularly become a cost issue for developers when unforeseen costs for mitigation works are claimed by contractors, or watching briefs cause construction work to be stopped/delayed. Archaeology is one of the key ground condition issues that the developer should seek to transfer or actively manage with a main works contractor depending on the chosen form of main contract.

In the ECC example (see key guidance), risk is shared between the contractor (who takes on the risk of dealing with foreseeable finds) and the employer who accepts the costs for unforeseeable finds. Developers need to be fully aware of how these terms are defined to ensure that compensation event resolution does not lead to dispute. In the example shown costs for remediation works for unforeseeable finds were defined in the contract and recorded as likely to be met by the employer.

4.8.4 Defining the unforeseen, unforeseeable and unexpected

Where contracts contain clauses covering the treatment of unexpected finds, disputes can arise where those terms are poorly defined and where the risk share is unclear for particular situations. The key issue is that unexpected does not mean that the finds were unforeseeable. Neither does unforeseen mean that the finds were unforeseeable.

Key guidance: example Highways Agency ECC contract

Engineering and construction contracts (ECC) have sought to aid resolution of numerous compensation claims from contractors by defining the key terms:

- foreseeable finds – discoveries of significant archaeological material that occur in the mitigation and/or construction phases that could have been predicted using professional judgment from the information provided by the employer in the tender documents. The costs are likely to be borne by the contractor

- unforeseeable finds – discoveries of significant archaeological material that occur in the mitigation or construction phases of a scheme despite the reasonable and professionally competent interpretation of all the documents and materials, including the outline archaeological design brief made available by the employer in the tender documents. The costs are likely to be borne by the employer.

Definition of terms in this way has been successful to an extent, however note that professional judgement is still the subjective issue upon which many compensation claims can become unstable.

Key issues: contract forms

◆ standard forms provide the best protection against dispute for all parties

◆ all contract forms should include a comprehensive schedule of rates to effectively manage change and variations

◆ bills of quantities provide the best method of breaking down the works into manageable costed items either through applying a rate or lump sum

◆ professional services agreements are suitable for archaeological consultancy commissions but cannot effectively substitute for standard forms for undertaking investigation and mitigation works

◆ contract definitions for dealing with unforeseen ground conditions and archaeology need to be properly defined.

Checklist: controlling the processes

◆ consider archaeology at the earliest opportunity in the development process, preferably before site purchase

◆ consult with the heritage bodies and with county/unitary/local authority officers at the earliest opportunity

◆ understand how archaeology fits into the development and construction process, and into the planning process

◆ understand each role in the process, and how it relates to other members of the project team, and the regulatory authorities

◆ take independent specialist advice where necessary

◆ use only suitably experienced and reputable archaeological consultants and contracting organisations

◆ have regard to the contractual arrangements chosen to regulate archaeological works

◆ involve archaeologists in design teams

◆ involve archaeologists in risk assessments

◆ provide archaeological information to planning or statutory regulators in a timely manner

◆ ensure compliance with all relevant legislation

◆ follow the terms of any Scheduled Monument or listed building or other consents that may apply

◆ follow the terms of any planning conditions, planning obligations (Section 106 agreements) etc that may apply

◆ follow good practice guidance on managing on-site archaeological works

◆ conduct sufficient appraisal and assessment (pre-determination) investigations to achieve understanding and control over the archaeological strategy for the construction stages of the project.

Finally:

◆ acknowledge the unknown and make contingencies for unexpected discoveries

◆ follow this guidance, particularly regarding the processes of risk assessment and management (Section 3.1)

◆ take a proactive approach to archaeology

◆ consider how following good practice can contribute to the project – by managing financial, commercial and programme risks caused by archaeology and by making positive contributions to the project.

Archaeology and development

5   Achieving good practice

This section is intended to give further practical advice through documented case studies of how aspects of the processes set out in this guide have been put into practice to achieve the most advantageous outcomes for both the development sector and the cultural heritage assets. Both will benefit the wider community.

The good practice examples given here are, where possible, cross referenced to readily available detailed guidance on aspects of archaeology and development published by government, public institutions, professional organisations and heritage bodies. These are listed in the References section. Although the main benefits of a proactive and managed approach to archaeology in a development context lie in reducing potential risks to the project, it is important to note that archaeology can have many positive affects.

5.1   EARLY RISK ASSESSMENT

A constant theme of this guide has been the importance of considering archaeological risk at the earliest opportunity (Case studies 5.1 and 5.2).

Case study 5.1   *Merton Abbey Mills*

Background

At Merton Abbey Mills, LB Merton, the developers, Countryside Properties, and their design team involved archaeologists from the earliest stages in the planning process to gather new evidence, using both non-intrusive and intrusive means, to assess the survival of archaeological remains at the site.

Outcome

This information was used to facilitate the design of a scheme that would both satisfy the requirements of the developer and safeguard the heritage of the site. With good communication, both the main contractor and archaeological team worked together effectively to allow construction to progress while taking into account archaeological requirements. In this case preserving medieval remains *in situ*, and excavating later archaeological remains in limited areas where preservation was not possible (Figure 5.1).

Lesson learned

♦ integration of archaeological specialists into design teams at the earliest stages of a project is key to the design and implementation of mitigation schemes.

Figure 5.1   Excavation in progress at Merton Abbey Mills (courtesy MoLAS)

(source: MoLAS)

Background

The redevelopment of two major London hospitals took many years to plan, first under the NHS Hospital Trusts and then as part of a private finance initiative (PFI) scheme. A central concern was the need to design a rolling programme of demolition and construction that would allow each site to continue to function as work progressed. The developers recognised from the outset that it was important to minimise the risk of delays during construction and chose to involve an archaeological contractor in planning and assessment from the outset.

Outcome

A phase of desk-based assessment highlighted the potential for archaeological remains on both sites and allowed an initial assessment of the probable impacts from the outline proposals. To define what actually survived, a programme of phased evaluations took place. This part of the process took several years (alongside other environmental assessments and development design work) due to the restrictions of working within the operational hospitals.

Assessment and evaluation work indicated that below-ground archaeological survival (and risk) was focused on only a small area at each of these large sites: a cemetery at the Royal London (Case study 5.8) and the ditch which ran around the medieval City Wall at St Bart's. With these areas defined, the developer was able to continue with design and redevelopment over much of the site knowing that foreseeable archaeological risk had been reduced. Continuing archaeological work at the two sites has concentrated on devising, negotiating and implementing a mitigation strategy for the small areas where archaeology was an issue.

In addition, to secure preservation by record of those buildings and parts of buildings that were of architectural and historic interest, and which were to be demolished or substantially altered, a campaign of building recording was commissioned at the Royal London. The main aims were to investigate and analyse the physical fabric of the existing buildings, record them to an appropriate level of detail, illustrate evidence for construction, development and use, and take account of documentary sources for the history and use of the buildings. Both listed and unlisted buildings were surveyed due to their group value and because they lay within a conservation area.

Lessons learned

Integrating archaeology into the design of complex redevelopment programmes:

◆ reduces the risk of unforeseen delays

◆ highlights potential risks and allows them to be managed effectively.

(source: MoLAS/Skanska)

5.2   THE PROCESSES IN PRACTICE: DESIGN OF A MITIGATION STRATEGY

Even areas known to contain extensive and important archaeological remains can be successfully developed, with a flexible approach to design and co-operation between archaeologists, curators, planners and developers from the early stages.

Background

The Northgate development is an example of a large regeneration project in an historic urban centre. The 4.6 ha development has an estimated cost (2006) of £300m and is a joint development between Chester City Council and ING Real Estate. It involves the construction of a new library, market, performing arts centre, bus station, department store, shops and residential units.

Outcome

The City Council, advised by its archaeology service, prepared a design brief in 1999. Existing information allowed them to grade the development area into four levels of archaeological significance, which ranged from those where previous development had destroyed all archaeology and there was no obstacle to development, to areas where archaeological remains were known to be so well preserved and significant that no development impacts should be permitted.

With this as a guide, the developer's structural engineer and archaeological consultant, working with English Heritage and the City Council's archaeology service were able to collaborate on a design solution that would meet the developer's requirements, but minimise archaeological impacts. The traffic flow through the development was totally reconfigured to avoid cutting through buried Roman defences. Basements and other major intrusions were sited in areas of existing disturbance, with widely spaced bored piles in areas of well preserved remains. Results of archaeological evaluation trenches and geophysical survey fed into the detailed design of foundations and floor slabs of each building.

The design exercise produced an engineering appraisal document setting out the mitigation strategy for each building or area, and the percentage of its footprint that will be damaged by groundworks. A figure of 1.1–2 per cent was attained for most buildings. Where additional disturbance was unavoidable, impacts were confined to areas where the archaeological deposits were known to have been damaged by previous development. Excavation or watching brief by an independent archaeological contractor will take place in those areas.

The archaeological strategy was secured by an archaeological planning condition and a Section 106 Agreement.

Lessons learned

◆ the design of a successful mitigation scheme depends on the early involvement and close co-operation of a wide range of professionals and specialists from the heritage bodies, planning authorities, development/design team and archaeological contractors.

A flexible approach is required from the archaeological profession, with mitigation options clearly tied to actual archaeological survival and likely development impacts.

(source: IFA/Chester Archaeology Service)

5.3   THE PROCESSES IN PRACTICE: LINEAR SCHEME

Case study 5.4 shows how the processes described in Chapter 4 operate in the context of a linear development, and in this case a pipeline project. The developer has permitted development rights (Section 2.5.6), but follows environmental good practice with regard to archaeology.

Background

Thames Water proposed to construct an ALF (alleviation of low flows) pipeline in the Darenth Valley. Although the pipeline is permitted development and does not require planning permission, Thames Water adheres to the terms of the code of practice on conservation, access and recreation, published as a result of the Water Act 1989, because its activities may affect the historic landscape. An archaeological contractor was commissioned to carry out an archaeological watching brief or strip map and sample investigation along the 7 km long pipeline route.

Outcome

Following initial desk-based assessment, archaeological evaluation took place along selected parts of the route to identify any archaeological hot spots before construction started, and to allow for necessary archaeological excavation to be included in the construction programme. The techniques adopted were field walking and geophysical surveys.

Significant archaeological remains were uncovered where the route passed to the north of the Darenth Roman villa. A four week excavation with up to six archaeologists recorded a road, ditches, postholes and pits, relating to activity in the enclosures outside the villa complex.

Along the rest of the route, the archaeological watching brief comprised the monitoring of topsoil/subsoil stripping of the 20 m-wide easement, with additional monitoring of the pipe trench excavations. Isolated archaeological features were rapidly recorded and investigated as the stripping progressed along the route (Figure 5.2). The archaeological features were planned using a computerised recording system, and the areas of investigation located by GPS.

Lessons learned

♦ field assessment in advance of the scheme is key to avoiding delays from unexpected discoveries

♦ technological solutions can enable rapid recording of simple archaeological remains encountered during watching briefs on construction.

Figure 5.2
Archaeological recording within the pipeline easement (courtesy MoLAS)

(source: MoLAS)

5.4   THE PROCESSES IN PRACTICE: COASTAL AND MARINE SCHEME

Certain legal constraints and technical difficulties are specific to the development or exploitation of coastal and marine sites, and specialist advice should always be sought from an archaeologist with relevant expertise (Case study 5.5). However, the basic principles of risk assessment and the staged process of archaeological assessment, evaluation and mitigation are similar to purely land-based projects (English Heritage, 2006b or c).

Background

The wreck of an early seventeenth century vessel was discovered in the Swash Channel at the entrance to Poole Harbour, Dorset during geophysical investigations carried out as part of the archaeological assessment for a channel deepening scheme. The examination of the wreck and related debris later on merited emergency designation in December 2004 under the Protection of Wrecks Act 1973 due to its archaeological significance, and in particular the remarkable survival and condition of the largely coherent hull structure.

Outcome

The archaeological examination of the site concluded that it was under threat of exposure and deterioration due to dynamic seabed conditions and from the proposed dredging. About two hundred sandbags were installed on the site by diving archaeologists to protect the exposed remains. The stabilised site was photographically recorded for monitoring purposes. Due to the statutory protection afforded to the site, all works within the designated area of the wreck requires a licence from the Secretary of State for Department of Culture, Media and Sport. However, positive engagement with the Poole Harbour Commissioners from an early stage has meant that the mitigation project proposal with clear archaeological objectives was developed and implemented. Such a case study demonstrates that mitigation is possible and that a negotiated outcome to the satisfaction of English Heritage and developers could be achieved.

Lessons learned

♦ marine sites require specific expert knowledge and services

♦ the basic principles of risk assessment and the staged process of archaeological assessment, evaluation and mitigation of coastal and marine sites apply equally to marine and terrestrial projects.

5.5   THE PROCESSES IN PRACTICE: PHASED ARCHAEOLOGY AND CONSTRUCTION

Ideally archaeological works including excavation would take place before the groundworks and construction teams arrived on site. Where possible, it can reduce risks caused by delays, health and safety issues related to the separation of activities and personnel, and cut down the complexity of the construction programme. On many developments, programme windows are so tight that it is often necessary for archaeology and construction to progress across the site in a phased manner. Many archaeological excavations require substantial enabling works (such as dewatering or ground reduction and shoring), which can only logistically be carried out as part of the main site works. Case study 5.6 is an urban example, but the principle can be applied to any large development scheme.

Background

This large office and retail development by Land Securities Plc took place on a large site known to contain complex and important archaeology (the waterlogged remains of a first century AD Roman quay and associated warehouses). These remains would be time consuming to excavate, but preservation *in situ* was not a solution that could be accommodated into the development design.

Outcome

Following a desk study, an archaeological evaluation (trial trenching) took place from April to May 1994 before construction. This work clarified the actual nature and survival of the on-site archaeology, and helped with the detailed design of the new foundations and of the construction/archaeological excavation programme.

Excavation took place from January 1995 to February 1996. First a watching brief was held on the guide trench for a secant pile wall. As this was constructed, ground reduction to the top of archaeological deposits begun, allowing archaeological excavation to start across the northern part of the site. Once this area was cleared of archaeology, construction began in earnest on the northern half of the site, and the archaeologists moved onto the cleared southern half.

Lesson learned

For large and complex developments, a carefully planned, phased approach to archaeology and construction may be adopted to compress the overall archaeological delay to the development programme.

(source: MoLAS)

5.6   THE PROCESSES IN PRACTICE: MANAGEMENT OF MITIGATION ON SITE

Case study 5.7   *Gloscat, Gloucester*

Background

In 2003 Scott Wilson Ltd were commissioned as archaeological consultant for the Gloscat development in Gloucester. The proposed site comprised the development of a new college campus on a site that was adjacent to a Scheduled Monument, Llanthony Secunda Priory. Only remnant building remains of the priory complex were still standing and the location of the main priory buildings was unknown. The key risk issue was that any structures found in the development area that were associated with the Priory would be of national importance and so significant residual risk was attached to the development proposal. A detailed desk-based assessment was carried out to fully understand the site history and identify the potential for archaeological remains surviving on specific parts of the site.

Outcome

To define the character and extent of significant archaeological remains on the site a detailed field evaluation assessment was undertaken with trial trenches. This revealed that although considerable modern disturbance was evident, discrete but significant remains, associated with the foundations of the precinct buildings, survived on the site.

The results of the evaluation were reviewed against the proposed detailed development plans and potential design conflicts and opportunities for preservation *in situ* were identified. The development foundation design was altered to minimise impact on the archaeological remains and a mitigation strategy agreed with the local authority archaeologist for full excavation of those parts of the site that could not be preserved.

During the mitigation phase previously unidentified contaminated ground and utility services were identified that required rapid revision to the proposed archaeological design for mitigation works. This situation needed a fast and proactive resolution between the developers' designer, archaeologist and local authority archaeologist to adjust the parameters of the mitigation programme addressing these unexpected constraints. Further design changes were made that achieved a mitigation strategy suitable for all parties.

This would not have been possible without effective project risk management processes being in place to quickly address the required design changes.

Lessons learned

◆ unexpected ground conditions can affect the progress of agreed mitigation strategies

◆ a well-prepared and integrated team can address design changes with minimal impact on the overall project outcome.

Figure 5.3   *Archaeological work and site clearance underway at Gloscat, Gloucester (courtesy Scott Wilson Ltd)*

(source: Scott Wilson Ltd)

5.7   THE PROCESSES IN PRACTICE: HUMAN REMAINS

Specialist archaeological advice is essential when dealing with human remains on development sites, both to negotiate the legal issues and to determine an appropriate strategy.

Case study 5.8   *Royal London Hospital*

Background

An archaeological contractor was involved from the early stages of planning for the redevelopment of the Royal London Hospital, both to provide advice and undertake field investigations. Desk-based assessment and field evaluation established that the main archaeological risk came from the presence beneath a small part of the site of an 18th century cemetery. Evaluation showed that the burials were of particular importance for the evidence of 18th century surgical practices and evidence for medical conditions that the skeletons displayed.

Outcome

The contractor provided advice on how best to integrate excavation of the cemetery into the demolition and construction programme, which was critical on this site as the hospital had to remain open during a rolling redevelopment. Following the evaluation, the contractor was able to negotiate with English Heritage (GLAAS) that part of the cemetery would need to be archaeologically excavated to provide a representative sample of the buried population. Some 500 burials were later excavated carefully by archaeologists, fully recorded and removed for post-excavation assessment and analysis. The remaining cemetery areas threatened by the development were cleared more rapidly by a specialist cemetery clearance company without the need for archaeological recording.

Lessons learned

◆ excavation of complex deposits such as human burials requires careful project design to avoid delays to development programmes.

Given sufficient information and specialist advice, the heritage bodies and LPA archaeology officers may be prepared to accept that only a sample of early modern cemetery populations require archaeological excavation and analysis.

(source: MoLAS/Skanska)

5.8   THE PROCESSES IN PRACTICE: OFF-SITE

Developers are held responsible for the off-site costs of archaeological works arising from on-site archaeological works (post-excavation work). These costs will depend on the significance of the archaeological deposits encountered. The minimum is the creation of a stable archive of records, analysis and reports, artefacts and ecofacts and its deposition with a suitable body for long-term curation and accessibility to future researchers (eg IFA in prep and Walker, 1990).

Current guidance across the UK is strongly influenced by English Heritage's *Management of research projects in the historic environment* (2006), which supersedes (MAP2) *Management of archaeological projects 2* (1991). It defines several distinct stages to the post-excavation process (Section 4.7). Following excavation comes a stage of post-excavation assessment to determine the significance of the site and the excavated material, and to determine the potential of the data for further analysis, publication and/or archiving. A post-excavation assessment report is produced and if further work is thought to be required, an updated project design (UPD) setting out proposals and costs for analysis and publication.

MAP2 sets out good practice, but it is not intended to be followed mechanically particularly in the case of smaller or less significant sites. In all cases the actual cost to the developer, and the amount of analysis and the form of publication (archive reports, web-based presentations, popular leaflets or books, articles in academic journals, academic monographs etc), can only be accurately costed at the stage of the UPD (Case study 5.9).

Once the UPD is produced the form, content and budget for the analysis and publication stage is often subject to further negotiation between the archaeological consultant/contractor and the local authority archaeology officer (and the statutory authorities if they were involved in the project). Despite all this it remains common practice that many developers insist on guarantees of maximum post-excavation costs at an earlier stage to assist with future budgeting. Depending on the significance of the findings, different approaches may be taken as shown in Case studies 5.8 and 5.9.

Archaeology and development

Background

Between 1992 and 1998 the £2.76 billion Jubilee Line Extension Project was the largest civil engineering project in Europe. Running through Westminster and north Southwark, it traverses some of the most archaeologically sensitive areas of London, ending up at Stratford on the site of a medieval abbey (Figure 5.4). The tunnels for the Jubilee Line are deep, passing below any archaeological remains. However the new ticket halls, escalator shafts, ventilation shafts, grouting shafts and escape shafts, the diversion of countless services, the construction of new buildings and the underpinning of existing ones all required initial assessment followed, where appropriate, by evaluation and excavation.

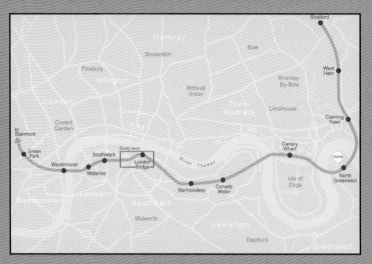

Figure 5.4   Route of the Jubilee Line Extension (courtesy MoLAS)

Outcome

The assessment and evaluation phases were carried out ahead of construction and the development programme was flexible enough to accommodate several major excavations where significant archaeology was encountered (including nationally significant Roman roadside buildings at London Bridge and an internationally significant medieval abbey and cemetery at Stratford). Three archaeological organisations were involved, one of which had overall managerial responsibility to ensure contract and programme compliance.

Each of the major sites required full post-excavation assessment reports, programmes of analysis and later monograph publications, which would take many years to complete (the seventh and final volume was published in 2005). To allow the results to be made public (and to spread awareness of both the construction scheme and London Underground Limited's support for the historic environment while construction was still in progress), a popular booklet was produced in 1998 (Figure 5.5 and Drummond-Murray *et al*, 1998). This describes the main findings in non-technical language, illustrated in colour and designed to reach a wide audience.

Figure 5.5

Cover of popular book
The Big Dig (MoLAS)

Lessons learned

◆ given sufficiently early assessment and evaluation, and a flexible approach to programming complex projects, even major archaeological excavations sites can be successfully incorporated into development programmes with minimal delays

◆ archaeologists may be able to produce information for print or web distribution to inform and enthuse the public for the archaeological findings and the development scheme, while construction work is still ongoing.

(source: MoLAS)

Background

Assessment, evaluation and excavation were required by the planning authority in advance of the redevelopment of a small site in Southwark, London.

Outcome

The archaeology uncovered was well preserved (the remains of a 17th to late 18th century tannery), but it was concluded that the find was of largely local significance and interest – relevant to the post-medieval development of Bermondsey's leather industry. A seven page report was prepared and published in the local archaeological journal. Southwark/Bermondsey was an important leather producing area in England and archaeological evidence for this industry is well preserved in the locality.

Lesson learned

Sites with locally significant remains may still reflect regional importance and require appropriate publication.

(source: MoLAS)

5.9   RISK MANAGEMENT: THE UNEXPECTED

Despite comprehensive risk assessment, archaeological discoveries cannot always be predicted in advance, so a flexible approach and the need for advice to resolve archaeological issues at the earliest opportunity and to consider the costs/benefits of archaeological risk insurance is necessary.

Case study 5.11   *172–176 The Highway, London*

Background

Early archaeological risk assessment and the involvement of an archaeological consultant had alerted the developer of this site in East London to the fact that Roman archaeology might be an issue as buildings, quarries and human burials had been previously found nearby. This was confirmed following a field evaluation. The local planning authority granted planning permission for a multi-storey residential development with piled foundations, subject to a condition for archaeological excavation and recording.

Outcome

As the archaeological excavation began it became apparent that the quality and extent of the Roman remains was far greater than had been indicated in the initial work: the southern part of the site contained a Roman bathing establishment with masonry surviving up to 1.75 m high (Figure 5.6). The English Heritage (GLAAS) curator considered the find to be of national importance, requiring preservation *in situ* and scheduling.

Figure 5.6   The unexpected and extensive remains of a Roman bathhouse (Pre-Construct Archaeology Ltd)

Archaeology and development

With a sensible risk management system in place, the archaeological consultant was able to negotiate a solution acceptable to both the developer and the archaeological curators. It was agreed that the structural remains would be preserved *in situ*, but that piles would be permitted in certain areas between the Roman walls, where floors and other elements of the bathhouse had been removed in antiquity. This was achieved by careful tie-in of the archaeologists' digital plans and the developer's site survey/design drawings. The remains were covered in inert sand and then spoil from the site in advance of piling.

Lessons learned

◆ the risk of unexpected archaeological discoveries cannot always be eliminated, even when good practice is followed

◆ however, with good management and communications in place, developers, archaeological consultants and archaeological contractors can work together with planning and statutory curators to achieve design solutions acceptable to all parties, even in difficult situations.

(source: English Heritage)

Case study 5.12   *The Newport boat*

Background

In June 2002 work was underway for the building of a new arts centre in Newport. An archaeological watching brief was carried out, as there was the potential for archaeological remains but the archaeologists were not expecting a large or important find: a 25 m merchant vessel from the medieval period (1465–1466) that was quickly identified as being of national importance (Figure 5.7), was uncovered.

Figure 5.7   *The Newport boat, during excavation (Glamorgan Gwent Archaeological Trust)*

Outcome

Initially it was agreed that once the boat had been uncovered only five per cent of the total timber would be lifted for analysis resulting in the destruction of the rest of the boat. The local press published an article on the find and massive public protest ensued. As a result of the protest, work stopped between June and November 2002 to recover more timbers from the vessel on the site.

Initial negotiations between the developer and the statutory bodies took three months before it was finally agreed that the National Assembly for Wales would fund the lifting, conservation and display of the vessel. The Glamorgan Gwent Archaeological Trust were initially given three weeks to excavate the boat but further public protest allowed the time period to be increased to 12 weeks.

The costs to the developer have been (conservatively) estimated as:

◆ unexpected excavation costs (for five weeks) £102 000

◆ constructing a public viewing platform £6000

◆ delay costs: unknown but possibly c£150 000.

Lesson learned

◆ it is advisable to plan for unexpected discoveries

◆ the effect of public opinion should not be underestimated.

In this case, the assessment of the site had raised the possibility of significant remains near the site of the medieval port. However it was not anticipated that the deep excavations for an orchestra pit would almost exactly coincide with the 25 m hull of a medieval boat.

(source: Jay Carver, Scott Wilson Ltd)

5.10   BURIED AND STANDING BUILDING ARCHAEOLOGY ON THE SAME SITE

It is often the case, where standing remains in the form of historic structures, listed buildings, or monuments are indicated in initial site appraisals or risk assessments, that the risk of associated buried archaeological remains will also need to be considered. Case study 5.13 is an example of how standing and buried archaeological remains may be efficiently and effectively investigated as part of an integrated programme by the same archaeologists.

Case study 5.13   *Torre Abbey, Devon*

Background

Torre Abbey, Torquay, is a former medieval religious house converted into a mansion in the early 16th century. The surviving buildings are now a museum, with ruins standing in a landscaped garden. The site also contains buried archaeological remains and important, historic standing buildings. Urgent conservation work on the standing fabric, combined with the construction of new visitor facilities was carried out by the local authority. An archaeological contractor acted as consultant to the project, with necessary work funded by Torbay Council and the Heritage Lottery Fund.

Outcome

The archaeologist was able to provide an integrated service to the local authority, advising the local museums service and their architects, negotiating with the statutory authorities, and providing staff for the necessary archaeological interventions (excavation, survey and standing building specialists). Much of this work was designed into the overall programme of works, such as the excavation of the cloister area in advance of new construction (Figure 5.8), and recording the standing west range of the abbey before its consolidation (Figure 5.9). A co-operative and flexible approach from the entire project team was essential as structural problems and archaeological discoveries were frequent occurrences in the course of building works – to be expected when dealing with an 800 year old structure that had seen many undocumented repairs and alterations. For example, building contractors discovered a large void beneath the timber floor, which the archaeological building specialists were able to identify as part of the chimney and fireplace of the medieval kitchen, long since bricked up and forgotten.

Lessons learned

◆ buried remains and standing buildings may all be significant parts of the historic environment

◆ investigations into standing historic buildings and below-ground archaeological remains, although requiring different specialists can be integrated.

Figure 5.8

Excavation in the cloister with grave slab and ruins (courtesy MoLAS)

Figure 5.9

Standing building recording (courtesy MoLAS)

(source: MoLAS)

97

5.11 PRESERVATION *IN SITU*: RE-USE OF PILED FOUNDATIONS

Although piling may be seen as an acceptable minimum impact foundation solution in many situations, curators are becoming increasingly concerned about the cumulative impacts from piling during successive developments on the same site. This is particularly important now, with buildings life cycles averaging only some 20–35 years. New piling impact within each development cycle would gradually destroy the entire site (Case study 5.14).

Case study 5.14   *The Collection, Lincoln*

Background

The Collection is a new museum, built in Lincoln on the site of a multi-storey car park built in 1970. The archaeological remains on the site were of national significance and so total re-use of the piles of the former building would have ensured that no further below-ground impacts to the archaeological deposits occurred.

Outcome

The car park pile layout had suited a rectangular building with even loading, whereas the new building had slightly different proportions, being designed as a sensitive addition to a historic townscape. In many cases new piles were needed.

Before the design stage of the redevelopment was finished and while the car park was still standing, a feasibility study was carried out to assess the potential for pile re-use. This study suggested that many of the piles on-site would be suitable for re-use, and that some records and original drawings for the building still existed. Where piles were deemed suitable for pile re-use, minor design changes were made to ensure that the old piles could be incorporated into the design. The old piles were subjected to non-invasive testing, which some initially failed, but passed following invasive visual inspection at 1–2 m depth. These inspections had some archaeological impacts, but were monitored as an archaeological watching brief.

Other methods were used to keep total disturbance from the new development below five per cent. During the design process, proposed new groups of four small diameter piles were changed to leave only a single large pile in each location. Piles were installed by a rig with a cutting tool, so that if any structural obstacles were encountered they could be bored through cleanly, rather than broken out. Except where cut out to take new piles, the ground slab from the car park was retained throughout the construction programme and within the new building, an important move that prevented construction damage to the medieval deposits beneath it.

Lessons learned

- total pile re-use is not always feasible, but even limited re-use reduces development impacts
- unless re-use of foundations is made compulsory compromise will probably be necessary. This could have been achieved by stipulating full re-use within the design brief
- however, the constraint of having to re-use existing piles would have added considerable risk to the success of the design and construction programme.

(source: English Heritage, 2007b)

Where the constraints imposed by re-using piled foundations can be accommodated, potential savings on archaeological excavation costs are significant, and archaeological remains are preserved *in situ* for future generations (Case study 5.15).

Given that techniques for preserving archaeology *in situ* are still in development (eg Corfield *et al*, 1998, Davis *et al*, 2004, Nixon, 2004), curators might consider the benefit of requiring long-term monitoring of ground conditions beneath such developments, as is the case at the Rose Theatre site (Case study 1.1). However, general practice is to seal any temporary monitoring points during the implementation of the mitigation scheme, as was carried out at the Globe Theatre site (Case study 5.16).

Background

The site lay within the medieval walled town, close to the river, in an area where well preserved, waterlogged archaeological remains were thought to survive. The concept of re-using foundations to preserve archaeology was promoted in a study of the archaeology of York (Ove Arup and Partners and York University in association with Bernard Thorpe, 1991) and is usually suggested as a mitigation option by the local curator.

Outcome

In this case, after initial consultation with the city council archaeologist, the developers proposed building off the foundation slab of the previous building, to reduce the potential costs of dealing with the archaeology. In one area, piles from the previous building were broken out, tested and determined to be suitable. The new design required only a few additional piles. Required archaeological work constituted a watching brief on the new pile caps and service runs.

Lessons learned

◆ re-using foundations places design constraints on architects and engineers (in this case it led to a departure from the normal layout of the hotel chain's other sites)

◆ cost savings may be significant, if it proves possible to avoid excavating sites with important, deeply stratified and well preserved archaeological remains.

(source: Williams and Butcher, 2006)

5.12   PRESERVATION *IN SITU*: POSITION OF PRESERVED REMAINS INDICATED IN DESIGN

Many archaeological remains, even those of international importance, may be too fragile for public display. Where these remains include waterlogged plant remains, timbers etc, which have to be preserved *in situ*, even exposing in a controlled archaeological excavation may hasten their destruction. In such cases the position of buried archaeological features may be reflected in development design (Case study 5.16).

Archaeology and development

Background

After the problems from the discovery of the contemporary Rose Theatre (Case study 1.1) the redevelopment of the Anchor Terrace Car Park in Park Street, Southwark, London, the documented site of Shakespeare's Globe Theatre, was always going to involve an imaginative solution. Early archaeological assessment of the site through targeted evaluation located a small part of the theatre, which was recorded, then covered over in a manner recommended by specialist environmental consultants to preserve the remains.

Outcome

There followed a long period of scientific data collection and analysis, including regular monitoring of site ground conditions by environmental scientists, further desk-based assessment, and negotiation, as the developer, MoLAS, the planning authority, English Heritage, and environmental scientists considered how best to proceed. The Globe Theatre was a Scheduled Monument. Furthermore the remains were waterlogged – well-preserved but fragile – vulnerable to any changes in water or oxygen level or soil chemistry. Further archaeological excavation would risk destroying the remains. To complicate matters, part of the theatre lay under a Grade II listed building.

By a process of negotiation and compromise, weighing the aspirations of the developer against the need to preserve the monument, a solution was reached. The listed building was refurbished with all its services running above ground, and a new residential block was constructed outside the scheduled area. Over the scheduled area a preservation backfill incorporating an impermeable barrier was laid down under archaeological and scientific supervision (Figure 5.10). No construction traffic was allowed within the monument, and the preservation backfill material was installed using a long-reach machine sitting beyond the scheduled area. The surface was then landscaped as a courtyard within the new development, with the position of the known theatre walls marked in coloured cobbles (Figure 5.11) and permanent display boards to interpret the site to visitors.

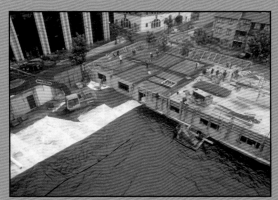

Figure 5.10

Installation of the impermeable barrier as part of the preservation backfill at the Globe Theatre site (courtesy MoLAS)

Figure 5.11 The position of the theatre walls indicated in the courtyard at the Globe Theatre site (courtesy MoLAS)

Lessons learned

◆ preservation *in situ*, even of fragile, internationally important archaeological remains, can be achieved by a collaborative approach between developers, archaeologists and specialist advisors

◆ techniques to achieve preservation *in situ* are still undergoing research and development. Many involve raising the ground (or basement/invert etc) level of the proposed development and covering the archaeological remains with a protective layer of inert sand and one or more geomembranes to protect it from the weight of overlying surfaces, pipe, plant, or traffic.

(source: MoLAS)

5.13 PRESERVATION *IN SITU*: DISPLAY OF ACTUAL ARCHAEOLOGICAL REMAINS

In exceptional cases archaeological discoveries may be not only important enough to merit preservation *in situ*, but also substantial and impressive enough to merit display as an historic attraction and focal point within a development (Case study 5.17).

Case study 5.17   *Spitalfields Charnel House*

Background

The regeneration of the Spitalfields area in east London was a complex series of development projects in an archaeologically sensitive area. A scheduled medieval hospital was just one of many constraints. Through the foresight of the Spitalfields development group and its partners and the early involvement of a competent archaeological contractor to liaise with the statutory and planning authorities, a phased programme of archaeological excavation and construction was agreed. Even the enormous medieval cemetery was predicted by early evaluation works. So when the detailed construction programme was agreed, the time needed for the excavation of some 10 500 human burials was written in and programme disruption avoided. In the middle of the cemetery, an exceptionally well preserved charnel house (a medieval chapel designed to store human bones) was found.

Outcome

The developer decided that the expense of preserving the building was justified compared with the difficulties of negotiating its destruction. The remains had to be protected from damage during the initial groundworks (Figure 5.12), while the designs were altered in this part of the site to allow the conservation and display of the medieval building in its own basement, accessible to all as a reminder of the site's history (Figure 5.13).

Lesson learned

♦ the foresight of the developer resulted in an important building being preserved and displayed – a historic focus within the development and an attraction to visitors and occupiers.

Figure 5.12

Protecting the charnel house during development at Spitalfields, London (courtesy MoLAS)

Figure 5.13 The charnel house as now displayed in the new Bishop Square development, Spitalfields, London (courtesy MoLAS)

(source: MoLAS)

Archaeology and development

In some situations (Case study 5.18) investment in the preservation and display of archaeological remains can provide a significant civic amenity (Figures 5.14 and 5.15).

Case study 5.18   *Welwyn Roman baths*

Background

Roman baths excavated near Welwyn, Hertfordshire (Figure 5.14) were found to be in the path of the planned new motorway section of the A1(M).

Outcome

After campaigning by local archaeologists a special chamber was constructed over the baths preserving them *in situ* 9 m beneath the motorway embankment. An access tunnel was fitted (Figure 5.15) and the chamber opened as a small museum in 1975.

Lesson learned

♦ an unusual and innovative approach to an archaeological discovery created a museum that has become a popular local amenity and is still in use today.

Figure 5.14

The hot room of the Welwyn Roman baths, as displayed (courtesy N Woodcraft)

Figure 5.15

The tunnel built to protect the remains seen before the formation of the motorway embankment (courtesy T Rook)

(source: CIRIA/Welwyn/Hatfield Museums Service)

5.14   BENEFITS OF PUBLIC INFORMATION AND EDUCATION

Integration of archaeology into the development process can make a positive contribution to society in terms of public information and education. Such contributions may bring additional benefits to developers.

On very large sites, controversial developments or where public interest is very high, it is worth considering investing in dedicated display space on or adjacent to the site, as well as an organised programme of public education, both during and after the excavations (Case study 5.19).

Case study 5.19   *Spitalfields visitor centre*

Background

The redevelopment of Spitalfields Market was not welcomed by all Londoners. The Spitalfields Development Group's regarded their support of archaeology as one of many ways they could demonstrate their commitment to the local community.

Outcome

As well as frequently updated display boards to keep people informed (Figure 5.16) the client's archaeological contractor took local groups, school parties and archaeological societies around the site by arrangement (Figure 5.17). The archaeologists built a visitor centre adjacent to the site, which attracted 27 000 visitors in a single summer (Figure 5.18). Television crews were welcomed and two major documentary programmes made for the BBC.

Sustainability was added by the preservation and display of the charnel house (Case study 5.17) within the finished development.

Lesson learned

♦ a relatively small investment in publicising their support of archaeology and encouraging local access and involvement, one way developers can improve their image with unsympathetic local communities.

Figure 5.16

Display panels are an inexpensive way of engaging with the public (courtesy MoLAS)

Figure 5.17 Archaeologist conducting a school party around an excavation (courtesy MoLAS)

Figure 5.18 Inside the Spitalfields visitor centre (courtesy MoLAS)

(source: MoLAS)

Archaeology and development

On smaller sites, the investment required for archaeologists to produce display boards to place at strategic points around a site hoarding or on a development/company website is relatively minor, but can have a major impact on public perceptions (Case study 5.20).

Case study 5.20   *Old Welsh Bridge/Frankwell Quay, Shrewsbury*

Background

During preliminary studies connected with the development of a new theatre in Shrewsbury it became apparent that the remains of a medieval fortified bridge were present on the site. It was decided to record, conserve and preserve *in situ* the surviving bridge arch and associated remains beneath the new development.

Outcome

The developer commissioned the archaeological contractor to produce information boards to place on the site hoarding. These served to inform the public of the important discoveries on-site and also to publicise the developer's intention to preserve the remains, and to inform people of the nature of the continuing development.

After agreement with the development and construction team and with careful consideration of health and safety issues, two very successful public open days were held over a weekend. Hundreds of interested local people paid a visit to the site and were given a tour by the archaeological site supervisors.

Lessons learned

- publicising archaeology also publicises the development
- it is important to inform the public regarding the treatment of remains they may have a connection to
- site tours, although rarely possible on construction sites, are often hugely popular with local communities.

(source: MoLAS)

5.15   COMMUNITY INVOLVEMENT

Archaeology may make an important contribution to the success of a regeneration project, particularly by forging connections with the local community (Case study 5.21).

Case study 5.21   *St Margaret's Almshouses, Taunton*

Background

St Margaret's Almshouses in Taunton were built in the early sixteenth century by Abbot Bere of Glastonbury and served as an almshouse until the 1930s. Before that the site was a leper hospital. When it ceased to be used as almshouses the building became occupied by community groups until the 1990s after which it was untenanted. Later the building was vandalised, subject to frequent stone throwing and suffered an arson attack.

Outcome

The Somerset Building Preservation Trust and West Somerset Housing Association redeveloped it for housing, using sympathetic design to ensure the historic building retained its character. Excavations were run as a training scheme for archaeology students, but pupils, teachers, parents and helpers from six local schools also participated. Regular open days were organised, and children visited during redevelopment to see craftsmen at work. As a result of the excavations, the remains of the chapel of St Margaret were located as well as traces of the original hospital.

Lessons learned

- public involvement in excavations can produce important archaeological information and a sense of local heritage for several thousand local people
- education and information may be a successful way of encouraging local people to care for elements of the built heritage, particularly in deprived areas.

(source: Homes with History, The Housing Corporation, English Heritage and the Institute of Field Archaeologists, 2003)

5.16   ONGOING POSITIVE PUBLICITY

Archaeological contractors can help to arrange public events and manage press releases to generate favourable media coverage for development and construction projects and the companies that carry them out (Case studies 5.22 and 5.23).

Case study 5.22   *30 St Mary Axe*

Background

In 1995, the remains of a young woman from the fourth century AD were excavated on the site of the Swiss Re Tower, 30 St Mary Axe, in the City of London (Figure 5.19).

Outcome

In 2007, after the construction and off-site archaeological process was completed, the managing director of the developer Minerva Plc arranged for the remains to be re-buried by the site where they were found, preceded by a simple service of commemoration attended by the Lady Mayoress of the City of London.

The reburial generated press and television interest, and media coverage noted how the commemoration of this unknown Roman Londoner speaks to future generations living and working in the City, bringing them closer to other Londoners. The marker that was erected at the site now serves as a direct link to the rich past of the city. Dave Shadwell, managing director of Skanska UK's Building Operating Unit stated: "whilst creating and constructing the modern skyscaper that is the London of today it is only right and fitting at the same time to recognise and maintain the history of London. This very personal project is a great example of how that can be achieved".

Lesson learned

◆ heritage has the potential to evoke a powerful sense of place and identity for the future.

Figure 5.19

History meets modern, 30 St Mary Axe (courtesy CIRIA)

(source: MoLAS/Skanska)

Background

For the British Land Company Plc, developers of this major site on Fenchurch Street, in the City of London, archaeology was one of the earliest considerations. Appropriate terms of reference were agreed with the City planners and MoLAS were appointed as archaeologists, working closely with the engineering team and archaeology consultant at Arup and with Skanska, the contractor appointed to carry out the site preparatory works. The mitigation strategy at this site involved a significant archaeological excavation, as well as the preservation *in situ* of a sample of archaeological deposits along one side of the site.

Outcome

The archaeological work unlocked invaluable information about Roman and medieval London. The developer asked MoLAS to create large information boards on the site hoarding to advise the public of new discoveries. One discovery in particular caught the public attention: the unexpected find of a cache of 43 Roman gold coins, which had lain concealed on the site for nearly 1800 years. The British Land Company took the opportunity to share the discovery not only with the public (the coins were displayed at the Museum of London), but also with the company's shareholders in a booklet summarising the find, and a reproduction Roman coin. The developer drew on the find and the rich history of the site in later marketing, which contributed to their annual report and to showcases such as the promotion at the annual property trade fair MIPIM.

Lesson learned

◆ archaeological discoveries can add a unique dimension to how a site, and its redevelopment, is perceived.

Key guidance: archaeological remains as a project asset

Good practice in the treatment of buried archaeological remains may make a positive contribution to a project and can contribute to a scheme's overall success by:

◆ the generation of favourable publicity for the scheme, the contractors and the developer

◆ demonstrating a commitment to sustainable development

◆ contributing a research dividend

◆ the incorporation of the archaeological findings within temporary hoarding designs or temporary exhibitions, viewing galleries etc

◆ the generation of community support

◆ the incorporation of actual archaeological remains within a scheme. Large structures may be preserved and displayed, and certain finds may be suitable for permanent display as an outstation of a local museum. Archaeological discoveries can be reflected in finished scheme designs or public artworks

◆ in very exceptional circumstances the display of archaeological remains can generate income

◆ popular interpretation and publication of the results of excavations can contribute to a community's sense of place and identity, and to local education programmes.

Do not underestimate less visible benefits. For example development/construction company staff will gain useful transferable skills from the experience of working alongside archaeological teams, particularly flexibility and innovation, but also increased satisfaction from participating in discovery and contributing to the public good.

Bibliography

AITCHISON, K (2002)
"The funding of professional archaeological practice in England"
Cultural Trends 39, Policy Studies Institute, London, pp 1–32

BADLG (1986)
British archaeologists' and developers' liaison group code of practice
Pub (01)11, British Archaeologists' and Developers' Liaison Group, London

BROWN D (2007)
Archaeological archives: a guide to best practice in creation, compilation, transfer and curation
Institute of Field Archaeologists on behalf of the Archaeological Archives Forum,
Reading (ISBN: 0-94839-391-2)
<http://www.archaeologists.net/modules/icontent/inPages/docs/pubs/Archives_Best_Pract
ice.pdf>

BUTCHER, A P, POWELL, J J M and SKINNER, H D (2006)
Re-use of foundations for urban site: a best practice handbook
IHS BRE Press, UK (ISBN: 978-1-86081-938-4)

CHAPMAN, T, ANDERSON S and WINDLE J (2007)
Reuse of foundations
CIRIA C653, London (ISBN: 978-0-86017-653-4)

CARTER, N and WILDE, L (2004)
*Environmental due diligence – the role of ISO 14015 in the environmental assessment of sites and
organisations*
BIP 2038, BSI Press, London

LAIDLER, D W, BRYCE, A J and WILBOURN, P (2002)
Brownfields – managing the development of previously developed land. A client's guide
CIRIA C578, London

CONNOLLY S and CHARLES, P (eds) (2005)
Environmental good practice on site
CIRIA C650, London

CORFIELD, M, HINTON, P, NIXON, T and POLLARD, M (eds) (1998)
"Preserving archaeological remains in situ"
In: *Proc conf Museum of London Archaeological Service, London, 1–3 April 1996*, pp 21–25

CORPORATION OF LONDON (2001)
The impact of archaeology on property developments in the City of London
London <http://www.cityoflondon.gov.uk>

CORPORATION OF LONDON (2004)
Planning advice note 3: Archaeology in the City of London: archaeology guidance
London <http://www.cityoflondon.gov.uk/plans/>

DAVIS, M J, GDANIEC, K L A, BRICE, M and WHITE L (2004)
Mitigation of construction impact on archaeological remains (2 vols)
Museum of London Archaeology Service, Pap/Com edition, London
(ISBN: 978-1-90199-247-2)

DCMS (2001)
The historic environment: a force for our future
Department for Culture, Media and Sport, London <http://www.culture.gov.uk>

DCMS (2006a)
Ecclesiastical exemption: the way forward
Department for Culture, Media and Sport, London <http://www.culture.gov.uk>

DCMS/WAG (2007)
Heritage protection for the 21st century
CM 7057, The Stationery Office Limited, London
<http://www.culture.gov.uk>

DMRB (1992–2007)
Design manual for roads and bridges (and subsequent advice notes)
Highways Agency, London

DRUMMOND-MURRAY, J, THOMAS, C and SIDELL, J, with MILES, A (1998)
The Big Dig: archaeology and the Jubilee Line Extension
Museum of London Archaeology Service, London (ISBN: 1-90199-205-5)
<http://www.museumoflondonarchaeology.org.uk>

ENGLISH HERITAGE

For more information visit: <http://www.english-heritage.org.uk>

Guide to the range of information required for consultations with English Heritage on proposals affecting nationally important heritage assets

Enabling development and the conservation of heritage assets: Policy statement, practical guide to assessment (2001)

Ancient monuments laboratory: geophysical survey in archaeological field evaluation (1995)

Taking to the water: English Heritage's initial policy for the management of maritime archaeology in England (2002)

New work in historic places of worship (2003a)

When English Heritage must be consulted on planning and listed building consent applications - a definitive guide – outside Greater London (2004)

Heritage Counts. The state of England's historic environment (2005)

Planning and development in the historic environment: a charter for English Heritage advisory services (2005)

Management of research projects in the historic environment. The MoRPHE project managers' guide, Swindon (2006a)

Ports: the impact of development on the maritime historic environment (2006b)

Conservation principles for the sustainable management of the historic environment (2006c)

Heritage Counts: England (2007a)

Guidance note 51352: Piling and archaeology (2007b)

Conservation principles: policies and guidance (2008)

ENGLISH HERITAGE AND THE CHURCH OF ENGLAND (2005)
Guidance for best practice for treatment of human remains excavated from Christian burial grounds in England
<http://www.english-heritage.org.uk/upload/pdf/16602_HumanRemains1.pdf>

EUROPEAN COMMISSION (2006)
The APPEAR method: A practical guide for the management of enhancement projects on urban archaeological sites
European Research Report 30/4 <http://www.in-situ.be/D30.3_sum_en.pdf>

GAFFNEY, C and GATER, J (2003)
Revealing the buried past: geophysics for archaeologists
The History Press Ltd, UK (ISBN: 978-0-75242-556-6)

HISTORIC SCOTLAND

Archaeological Procedure Paper 2 (1996a): *Project design, implementation and archiving*

Operational Policy Paper 2 (1996b): *Publication and archiving of archaeological projects*

Operational Policy Paper (2001): *Acquisition and disposal of artifacts*

Operational Policy Paper 5 (revised 2006a): *The treatment of human remains in archaeology*

Scheme to apply listed building control to exteriors of churches in ecclesiastical use: guidance notes (2006b)

HMSO (2000)
Environmental impact assessment: A guide to procedures
Department for Communities and Local Government, London (ISBN: 0-72772-960-8)

HSE (1991)
Protection of workers and the general public during the development of contaminated land
Guidance Note HS (G) 66-HMSO, HSE Books, Sudbury (ISBN: 0-11885-657-X)

HSE (1997)
Successful health and safety management, (2nd edition)
HSG65, HSE Books, Sudbury (ISBN: 0-71761-276-7)

HSE (2007)
Managing health and safety in construction. Construction (design and management) regulations 2007, (CDM) Approved code of practice
L144, HSE Books, Sudbury (ISBN: 978-0-71766-223-4)

IAI 2004 (1999)
The treatment of human remains: technical paper for archaeologists (revised)
Institute of Archaeologists of Ireland

ICE (1996)
Civil engineering procedure, 5th edition
Institution of Civil Engineers, London

ICE (2003)
Conditions of contract ground investigation, 2nd edition
Institution of Civil Engineers, London

ICE (2004a)
Conditions of contract for archaeological investigation, 1st edition. Conditions of contract, appendix and form of agreement for use in connection with archaeological investigation
Institution of Civil Engineers, London

Archaeology and development

ICE (2004b)
Guidance notes: *Conditions of contract for archaeological investigation*
Institution of Civil Engineers, London

ICE (2006)
Code of professional conduct
Revised edition, Institution of Civil Engineers, London

ICOMOS (1990)
Charter for the protection and management of the archaeological heritage
Archaeological Heritage Management <http://www.international.icomos.org>

IFA (1998)
Social housing development and archaeology: a report for the Housing Corporation South-East Regional Office
Institute of Field Archaeologists, Reading

IFA (2001a)
Standard and guidance for archaeological desk-based assessment
Revised edition, Institute of Field Archaeologists, Reading

IFA (2001b)
Standard and guidance for archaeological excavation
Revised edition, Institute of Field Archaeologists, Reading

IFA (2001c)
Standard and guidance for archaeological field evaluation
Revised edition, Institute of Field Archaeologists, Reading

IFA (2002)
Code of approved practice for the regulation of contractual arrangements in field archaeology
Revised edition, Institute of Field Archaeologists, Reading

IFA (2005a)
Regulations for the registration of archaeological organisations
Revised edition, Institute of Field Archaeologists, Reading

IFA (2005b)
Disciplinary regulations
Revised edition, Institute of Field Archaeologists, Reading

IFA (2006)
Code of conduct
Revised edition, Institute of Field Archaeologists, Reading

IFA (in prep)
Standard and guidance: archaeological archives: creation, preparation, transfer and curation
Institute of Field Archaeologists, Reading

IFA/IHBC/ALGAO (2007)
Standards and guidance for stewardship of the historic environment

KPMG (2004)
Impact: A survey on environmental due diligence
208-251, KPMG, London <http://www.kpmg.ch/library/pdf/20040514_KPMG_Survey_on_environmental_due_diligence.pdf>

MCCAFFREY, C, CHALLIS, K, CRANSTONE, D, TRUEMAN, M and NATHANAIL, C P (2005)
Guidance on assessing the risk posed by land contamination and its remediation on archaeological resource management
Science Report P5-077/SR, Environment Agency, Bristol (ISBN: 1-84432-080-4)

Newzeye (2006)
The developer's guide to brownfield - profits and pitfalls of brownfield development in the UK
<http://www.newzeyecentral.co.uk/Publications/tabid/151/agentType/View/PropertyID/1/Default.aspx>

NIXON, T (ed) (2004)
"Preserving archaeological remains *in situ*?"
In: *Proc of the 2nd conference 12–14 September 2001*, MoLAS surveys and handbooks series, London

NPPG5 (1998)
National planning policy guidance 5: *Archaeology and planning*
Scottish Executive, web only <http://www.scotland.gov.uk/Publications/1998/10/nppg5>

THORPE B (1991)
York development and archaeology study
Ove Arup and Partners and York University (out of print, copies available by request from City of York Council) <http://www.york.gov.uk>

PAN 42 (1994)
Planning advice note 42: *Archaeology – the planning process and scheduled monument procedures*
Scottish Office, Environment Department (ISBN: 0-74800-833-0)
<http://openscotland.gov.uk/Publications/1994/01/17081/21711>

PAN 58 (1999)
Planning advice note 58: *Environmental Impact Assessment*
Scottish Office, Environment Department
<http://www.scotland.gov.uk/Publications/1999/10/pan58-root/pan58>

Planning Policy Wales (2002)
National Assembly for Wales

PPG15 (1994)
Planning policy guidance 15: *Planning and the historic environment*
Communities and Local Government, London (ISBN: 0-11752-944-3)
<http://www.communities.gov.uk/publications/planningandbuilding/planningpolicyguidance8>

PPG16 (1990)
Planning policy guidance 16: *Archaeology and planning*
Communities and Local Government, London (ISBN: 0-11752-353-4)
<http://www.communities.gov.uk/publications/planningandbuilding/planningpolicyguidance9>

PPS6 (1999)
Planning policy statement 6: *Planning, archaeology and the built heritage*
Department of the Environment for Northern Ireland, Belfast
<http://www.planningni.gov.uk/AreaPlans_Policy/PPS/pps6/pps6.pdf>

PPS12 (2004)
Planning policy statement 12: *Local development frameworks*
Department for Communities and Local Government, London (ISBN: 978-0-11753-926-6) <http://www.communities.gov.uk/publications/planningandbuilding/pps12>

RIBA (2007)
RIBA Outline plan of work 2007
<http://www.ribabookshops.com>

ROBINSON, R (2002)
"Unexpected archaeological discovery insurance"
In: *Property Eye 6*, Aon Real Estate Practice, London, pp 4–5
<http://www.freemansguide.com>

WELSH OFFICE (2000)
Technical Advice Note (Wales) 6: *Archaeology and planning*
Revised <http://new.wales.gov.uk/topics/planning/policy/tans/tan6?lang=en>

THE HOUSING CORPORATION, ENGLISH HERITAGE and THE INSTITUTE OF
FIELD ARCHAEOLOGISTS (2003)
Homes with history
<http://www.archaeologists.net/modules/icontent/inPages/docs/pubs/homeswithhistory.pdf>

UNESCO (1972)
"UNESCO World Heritage Convention"
In: *Proc 17th general conf of the United Nations Educational, Scientific and Cultural
Organisation, the protection of the World Cultural and Natural Heritage Paris 17 Oct–21 Nov
1972* <http://whc.unesco.org/en/conventiontext/>

VALLETTA CONVENTION (1992)
Council of Europe Convention on the protection of the archaeological heritage
Council for Europe, Valletta, 16 January 1992
<http://fletcher.tufts.edu/multi/www/bh997.html>

WALKER, K (1990)
Guidelines for the preparation of excavation archives for long-term storage
United Kingdom Institute for Conservation (UKIC) Archaeology Section

WILLIAMS, T (ed) (1991)
Management of archaeological projects
English Heritage, London (ISBN: 1-85074-359-2)
<http://www.english-heritage.org.uk/publications>

WILLIAMS, J and BUTCHER, A P (2006)
"Foundation re-use as a mechanism for the preservation of buried cultural heritage in
urban centres: how new engineering research helps limit archaeological damage"
In: *Proc 7th European conf Saveur. Safeguarded cultural heritage, understanding viability for
the enlarged Europe, Prague, 31 May–3 June* pp 1230–1245
<http://www.arcchip.cz/ec-conference/presentations/Session%20II/1230-
1245%20williams.doc>

ACTS, CODES, DIRECTIVES, ORDERS AND REGULATIONS

Acts

Ancient Monuments and Archaeological Areas Act 1979 (c4), rev 1983 (as amended)
OPSI, London
<http://www.opsi.gov.uk/RevisedStatutes/Acts/ukpga/1979/cukpga_19790046_en_1>

Burial Act 1857 (c81)
OPSI, London
<http://www.opsi.gov.uk/RevisedStatutes/Acts/ukpga/1857/cukpga_18570081_en_1>

Care of cathedrals measure 1990 (No 2)
OPSI, London
<http://www.opsi.gov.uk/uk-church-measures/1990/Ukcm_19900002_en_1.htm>

Disused Burial Grounds Act 1884 (c72)
OPSI, London
<http://www.opsi.gov.uk/RevisedStatutes/Acts/ukpga/1884/cukpga_18840072_en_1>

Disused Burial Grounds (Amendment) Act 1981 (c18)
The UK Statute Law Database, London
<http://www.statutelaw.gov.uk>

Electricity Act (1989) (c29)
<www.uk-legislation.hmso.gov.uk/acts/acts1989/ukpga_19890029_en_1>

Highways Act 1980 (Gating Orders) (England) Regulations 2006
Statutory Instrument 2006 No. 537
<http://www.opsi.gov.uk/si/si2006/20060537.htm>

Merchant Shipping Act 1995 (c21)
OPSI, London <http://www.opsi.gov.uk/ACTS/acts1995/ukpga_19950021_en_1>

National Heritage Act 1983 (and subsequent amendments)
The UK Statute Law Database, London
<http://www.statutelaw.gov.uk>

Planning (Listed Buildings and Conservation Areas) Act 1990 (c9)
OPSI, London, <www.opsi.gov.uk/acts/acts1990/Ukpga_19900009_en_1.htm>

Planning (Listed Buildings and Conservation areas) (Scotland) Act 1997(c9)
OPSI, London <www.opsi.gov.uk/acts/acts1997/1997009.htm>

Protection of Wrecks Act 1973 (c33)
OPSI, London
<http://www.opsi.gov.uk/RevisedStatutes/Acts/ukpga/1973/cukpga_19730033_en_1>

Protection of Military Remains Act 1986 (Designation of Vessels and Controlled Sites)
Order 2006
Statutory Instrument 2006 No. 2616
OPSI, London <http://www.opsi.gov.uk/si/si2006/20062616.htm>

Treasure Act 1996 (c24) code of practice (2nd revision)
OPSI, London <http://www.opsi.gov.uk/Acts/acts1996/ukpga_19960024_en_1>

Water Act 1989 (c15)
OPSI, London <www.opsi.gov.uk/acts/acts1989/ukpga_19890015_en_1>

Archaeology and development

Codes

Code of Recommended Practice to the Pastoral Measure 1983 (as amended)
The Church Commissioners for England
<http://www.cofe.anglican.org/about/churchcommissioners/pastoral/pastadmin/code/>

Directives

EU Directive 2004
Environmental liability with regard to the prevention and remedying of environmental damage
Directive 2004//35/CE of the European Parliament and of the Council of 21 April 2004,
Official Journal of the European Union 30.04.2004, L143/56–75
<http://europa.eu/index_en.htm>

Orders

Ecclesiastical Exemption (Listed Buildings and Conservation Areas) Order 1994 No 1771
OPSI, London <www.opsi.gov.uk/SI/si1994/Uksi_19941771_en_1.htm>

Historic Monuments and Archaeological Objects (Northern Ireland) Order 1995 No 1625 (NI 9)
OPSI, London <www.legislation.gov.uk/si/si1995/Uksi_19951625_en_1.htm>

Town and Country Planning (General Permitted Development) Order 1995
Statutory Instrument 1995 No. 418
<http://www.opsi.gov.uk/si/si1995/Uksi_19950418_en_1.htm>

Regulations

Town and Country Planning (Churches, Places of Religious Worship and Burial Grounds) Regulations 1950, No 792
UNESCO, London
<http://www.unesco.org/culture/natlaws/media/pdf/gb/gb_town&countryplanning1950_engorof.pdf>

FURTHER READING

ANDRIKOPOULOU-STRACK, N, GHIGNY A-C, LETOR, A, MEGANCK, M, BOURGEOIS, J, PLUMIER, J, SAUNDERS, H, BLANCQUAERT, G and PRILAUX, G (2006)
Archaeological evaluation and aerial photography in the Planarch Area of North West Europe
Kent County Council/Planarch Partnership, Maidstone
<http://www.planarch.org/downloads/library/action_2b_final_report.pdf>

BADLG (1986)
British archaeologists' and developers' liaison group code of practice
Pub (01)11, British Archaeologists' and Developers' Liaison Group, London

BLANCQUAERT, G and MEDLYCOTT, M (2006)
Archaeological evaluation of rural areas in the Planarch Area of North West Europe
Kent County Council/Planarch Partnership, Maidstone
<http://www.planarch.org/downloads/library/action_2c_final_report.pdf>

Cadw (2002)
Ancient Monuments in Wales: Scheduled Monument Consent
2nd edition 2007, Cadw, Welsh Assembly Government, Cardiff
<http://www.cadw.wales.gov.uk/upload/resourcepool/Scheduled%20Monument%20Cons
ent%20booklet%20E6081.pdf> (ISBN: 978-1-85760-246-3)

DARVILL, T and FULTON, A (1998)
MARS: The monuments at risk survey of England, 1995: main report
Bournemouth and London, Bournemouth University and London

DCMS (2003)
Protecting our historic environment: making the system work better
Department for Culture, Media and Sport <http://www.culture.gov.uk/>

DCMS (2004)
Review of heritage protection: the way forward
Department for Culture, Media and Sport, London <http://www.culture.gov.uk/>

DCMS (2005)
Guidance for the care of human remains in museums
Department for Culture, Media and Sport, London <http://www.culture.gov.uk/>

DCMS (2006b)
Sustainable development action plan
Department of Culture Media and Sport, London
<http://www.defra.gov.uk/Environment/sustainable/action-plan.htm>

DOE

Circular 15/88 (1988): *Environmental assessment*
Circular 11/95 (1995): *The use of conditions in planning permissions*
HMSO, London

DYSON, L, JOHNSON, C, HEPPELL, E and PIETERS, M (2006)
Archaeological evaluation of wetlands in the Planarch Area of North West Europe
Kent County Council/Planarch Partnership, Maidstone
<http://www.planarch.org/>

EHTF (2000)
Archaeology in historic towns – a practical guide
Report 51, English Historic Towns Forum

ENGLISH HERITAGE

Power of place: the future of the historic environment (2000)

Managing local authority heritage assets: some principles for decision-makers (2003b)

Scheduled Monuments: a guide for owners and occupiers (2004)

*When English Heritage must be consulted on planning and listed building consent applications –
a definitive guide – inside Greater London* (2004)
<http://www.english-heritage.org.uk/upload/pdf/consult_london.pdf>

Understanding historic buildings: a guide to good recording practice (2006)
<http://www.english-
heritage.org.uk/upload/pdf/Understanding_Historic_Buildings_1.pdf>

GILMAN, P (2006)
Development of Sites and Monuments (SMRs) in the Planarch Area of North West Europe
Kent County Council/Planarch Partnership, Maidstone
<http://www.planarch.org/downloads/library/action_1a_final_report.pdf>

HEY, G and LACEY, M (2001)
Evaluation of archaeological decision-making processes and sampling strategies
Oxford Archaeological Unit/Planarch partnership, Oxford (ISBN: 0-90422-026-5)

HISTORIC SCOTLAND

Operational Policy Paper 6 (1999): *Conserving the underwater heritage*

*Passed to the future: Historic Scotland's policy for the sustainable management of the historic
environment* (2002)

Scottish Historic Environment Policy 2 (2006c): *Scheduling: protecting Scotland's nationally
important monuments*

Scottish Historic Environment Policy 1 (2007): *Scotland's historic environment*

HUNTER, J and RALSTON, I (eds) (1993)
Archaeological resource management in the UK: and introduction
Alan Sutton Publishing, Stroud (ISBN: 978-0-75091-607-3)

HUNTER, J and RALSTON, I (eds) (1999)
*The archaeology of Britain: an introduction from the upper palaeolithic to the Industrial
Revolution*
Routledge, London (ISBN: 0-41513-588-5)

IFA (2001)
Standard and guidance for archaeological watching brief
Revised edition, Institute of Field Archaeologists, Reading
<http://www.archaeologists.net/modules/icontent/inPages/docs/codes/watch_brief.pdf>

IFA, (2001)
*Standard and guidance for archaeological investigation and recording of standard buildings or
structures*
Revised edition, Institute of Field Archaeologists, Reading
<http://www.archaeologists.net/modules/icontent/inPages/docs/codes/build2.pdf>

IFA (2001)
*Standard and guidance for the collection, documentation, conservation and research of
archaeological materials*
Institute of Field Archaeologists, Reading <http://www.archaeologists.net>

JNAPC (2006)
Marine cultural heritage and seabed development: JNAPC code of practice for seabed development
Joint Nautical Archaeology Policy Committee, Crown Estates
<http://www.jnapc.org.uk/jnapc_brochure_may_2006.pdf>

JONES, C and SLINN, P (2006)
Cultural heritage and environmental impact assessment in the Planarch Area of North West Europe
Kent County Council/Planarch Partnership, Maidstone
<http://www.planarch.org/downloads/library/action_3a_final_report_english.pdf>

McMillon B (1991)
The archaeology handbook: a field manual and resource guide
John Wiley & Sons (ISBN: 978-0-47153-051-0)

MURNANE, E HEAP, A and SWAIN, A(2006)
Control of water pollution from linear construction projects. Technical guidance
CIRIA C648, London

ODPM

Planning guidance 20 (1992) : *Coastal planning*

Planning policy guidance 12 (1999): *Development plans*

Planning policy guidance 3 (2000): *Housing* (and subsequent revisions)

Planning policy statement 3 (2006): *Housing*

QAA (2006)
Subject benchmark statements Archaeology: Draft for consultation
Quality Assurance Agency for Higher Education <http://www.qaa.ac.uk/

RENFREW, C and BAHN, P (2004)
Archaeology: theories, methods and practice
4th edition, Thames and Hudson Ltd, London (ISBN: 978-0-50028-441-4)

RIPPON, S (2004)
"Historic landscape analysis: deciphering the countryside"
In: *Council for British Archaeology Practical Handbook 16*, York

THE HERITAGE COUNCIL (Ireland) (2000)
Archaeology and development: guidelines for good practice for developers
Prepared for the Heritage Council by the ICOMOS Irish Committee,
<http://www.heritagecouncil.ie/>

WAUGH, K (2006)
Archaeological management strategies in the Planarch Area of North West Europe
Kent County Council/Planarch Partnership, Maidstone
<http://www.planarch.org/downloads/library/action_3b_&_3c__final_report.pdf>

WESSEX ARCHAEOLOGY (2003)
Marine aggregate dredging and the historic environment. Assessing, evaluating, mitigating and monitoring the archaeological effects of marine aggregate dredging: Guidance note
Prepared on behalf of BMAPA and English Heritage <http://www.wessexarch.co.uk/>

Archaeology and development

USEFUL WEBSITES

APPEAR website
<http://in-situ.be/A_pres_overview.html>

Archaeoleg Cambria (Cambria Archaeology)
<http://www.cambria.org.uk>

Archaeology Data Service
<http://ads.ahds.ac.uk/>

Association of Local Government Archaeological Officers UK (ALGAO)
<http://www.algao.org.uk/>
A useful source of historic environment advice and links, and contacts for local government archaeology officers across the UK.

Council for British Archaeology (CBA)
<http://www.britarch.ac.uk/>
The website of a UK wide educational charity for the promotion of the historic environment. A good source of news, opinion, links, contacts and advice.

The Crown Estate
<http://www.thecrownestate.co.uk/>

Engineering and Construction Contracts (ECC)
<http://www.ecc.net/>

English Heritage
<http://www.english-heritage.org.uk/>

Greater London Archaeology Advisory Service
<http://www.english-heritage.org.uk/server/show/nav.8938>

Greater Manchester Archaeological Unit (GMAU)
<http://www.arts.manchester.ac.uk/umfac/>

Heritage Gateway
<http://www.heritagegateway.org.uk/>

Historic Environment Local Management (HELM) project
<http://www.helm.org.uk>
A collaborative venture between English Heritage, the DCMS, DCLG and DEFRA which aims to share best practice and build capacity and confidence in those dealing with the historic environment. The website is a useful source of case studies and policy statements produced by English Heritage, as well as guidance produced by English Heritage, HELM partners, local authorities, regional agencies and other key organisations.

International Council on Monuments and Sites (ICOMOS)
<http://www.international.icomos.org>

Institute of Field Archaeologists
<http://www.archaeologists.net/>
The website of the professional association for field archaeologists in England Wales and Scotland. A good source for news, guidance on professional standards and practice, with links to its Registered Archaeological Organisations (certified archaeological contractors).

Joint Contracts Tribunal Contracts (JCT)
<http://www.jctltd.co.uk>

Magic interactive map
<http://www.magic.gov.uk>

Maritime and Coastguard Agency
<http://www.mcga.gov.uk>

National Monuments Record of Wales
<http://www.coflein.gov.uk>

New Engineering Contracts (NEC)
<http://www.neccontract.com/contracts/>

Index of Archaeological Investigations (OASIS)
<http://oasis.ac.uk/>

Portable Antiquities Scheme
<http://www.finds.org.uk/>

The Royal Commission on the Ancient and Historical Monuments of Scotland
(RCAHMS)
<http://www.rcahms.gov.uk/>

The Royal Commission on the Ancient and Historical Monuments of Wales
(RCAHMW)
<http://www.rcahmw.gov.uk/>

World Heritage Sites
<http://whc.unesco.org>

UNESCO
<http://www.unesco.org/>

Ymddiriedolaeth Archaeolegol Morgannwg-Gwent (Glamorgan Gwent Archaeological
Trust)
<http://www.ggat.org.uk/>

Ymddiriedolaeth Archaeolegol Clwyd-Powys (Clwyd-Powys Archaeological Trust)
<http://www.cpat.org.uk/>

Ymddiriedolaeth Archaeolegol Gwynedd (Gwynedd Archaeological Trust)
<http://www.heneb.co.uk/>

A1   Government departments and national bodies

Welsh Assembly Government

Welsh Assembly Government
Cathays Park
Cardiff
CF10 3NQ
Tel: +44 (0)292 082 5111
Website: <http://www.wales.gov.uk/ >

Cadw
Welsh Assembly Government
Plas Carew
Unit 5/7 Cefn Coed
Parc Nantgarw
Cardiff
CF15 7QQ
Tel: +44 (0)1443 33 6000
Email: Cadw@Wales.gsi.gov.uk
Website: <http://www.cadw.wales.gov.uk>

Directorate for Culture, Welsh Language and Sport
Email: cswl@Wales.gsi.gov.uk

Department for the Environment, Planning and Countryside
Email: epc.requests@wales.gsi.gov.uk

Planning Division
Tel: +44 (0)292 082 5111
Planning.division@wales.gsi.gov.uk

Transport Wales
Rail and New Roads Division
Tel: +44 (0)292 082 6252

Roads Network Management Division
Tel: +44 (0)292 082 6249

Transport Planning and Administration Division
Tel: +44 (0) 292 082 3839

Scottish Executive
Tel: +44 (0)845 774 1741/(0)131 556 8400
Email: ceu@scotland.gsi.gov.uk
Website: <http://www.scotland.gov.uk/>

Development Department
Victoria Quay
Edinburgh
EH6 6QQ

Education Department
Scottish Executive
Victoria Quay
Edinburgh
EH6 6QQ

Enterprise, Transport and Lifelong Learning Department
Enterprise, Transport and Lifelong
Learning Department Secretariat
The Scottish Executive
6th Floor
Meridian Court
Cadogan Street
Glasgow
G2 6AT

Environment and Rural Affairs Department
Pentland House
47 Robb's Loan
Edinburgh
EH14 1TY

Northern Ireland Executive
Website:
<http://www.northernireland.gov.uk/>

UK government
Department for Communities and Local Government
Eland House
Bressenden Place
London
SW1E 5DU
Tel: +44 (0)207 944 4400
Fax +44 (0)207 944 9645
Email: contactus@communities.gov.uk
Website:
<http://www.communities.gov.uk/>

Department for Constitutional Affairs
Selborne House
54 Victoria Street
London
SW1E 6QW
Tel: +44 (0) 207 210 8500
Website: <http://www.dca.gov.uk>

Department for Culture, Media and Sport
(DCMS)
2–4 Cockspur Street
London
SW1Y 5DH
Tel: +44 (0) 207 211 6200
Email: enquiries@culture.gov.uk
Website: <http://www.culture.gov.uk>

Department for Environment, Food and
Rural Affairs (Defra)
Nobel House
17 Smith Square
London
SW1P 3JR
Tel: +44 (0) 845 933 5577
Fax: +44 (0)207 238 2188
Email: helpline@defra.gsi.gov.uk
Website: <http://www.defra.gov.uk>

Department for Transport (DfT)
Great Minster House
76 Marsham Street
London
SW1P 4DR
Tel: +44 (0)207 944 8300
Fax: +44 (0)207 944 9622
Website: <http://www.dft.gov.uk>

Environment Agency
Rio House
Waterside Drive
Aztec West, Almondbury
Bristol
BS32 4UD
Tel: +44 (0)870 850 6506 (general enquiries)
    +44 (0)800 807 060 (incident hotline)
Email:
enquiries@environment-agency.gov.uk
Website:
<http://www.environment-agency.gov.uk>

Forestry Commission
Silvan House
231 Corstorphine Road
Edinburgh
EH12 7AT
Tel: +44 (0)131 334 0303
Fax: +44 (0)131 314 6152
Email: enquiries@forestry.gsi.gov.uk
Website: <http://www.forestry.gov.uk>

Highways Agency
Tel: +44 (0)845 750 4030
Email: ha_info@highways.gsi.gov.uk
Website: <http://www.highways.gov.uk/>

Maritime and Coastguard Agency
Tutt Head
Mumbles
Swansea
West Glamorgan
SA3 4HW
Tel: +44 (0)870 600 6505
Website: <http://www.mcga.gov.uk>

Ministry of Defence (MoD)
The Ministerial Correspondence Unit
Floor 5, Zone A, Main Building
Whitehall
London
SW1A 2HB
Tel: +44 (0)870 607 4455
Website: <http://www.mod.uk>

Maritime and coastal archaeology
+ Powys, Flintshire, Wrexham and
Denbighshire
Tel: +44 (0)1443 33 6011

Guardianship, transport, forestry
+ Blaenau Gwent, Bridgend, Caerphilly,
Cardiff, Merthyr Tydfil, Monmouthshire,
Neath Port Talbot, Newport, Rhondda
Cynon Taff, Swansea, Torfaen, Vale of
Glamorgan
Tel: +44 (0)1443 33 6012

Post-excavation and publication, specialist
services, scheduling
+ Conwy, Gwynedd, Isle of Anglesey
Tel: +44 (0)1443 33 6010

Carmarthenshire, Ceredigion,
Pembrokeshire
Tel: +44 (0)1443 33 6013

Scheduled Ancient Monuments Record and
Inspectorate Support Section
Tel: +44 (0)1443 33 6073

Historic buildings listing
Tel: +44 (0)1443 33 6053

Historic Parks and Gardens
Tel: +44 (0)1443 33 6075

English Heritage
Website:
<http://www.english-heritage.org.uk/>

National Monument Record (NMR)
enquiries
Email: nmrinfo@english-heritage.org.uk
Tel: +44 (0)1793 414600

North East Region
Bessie Surtees House
41-44 Sandhill
Newcastle upon Tyne
NE1 3JF
Tel: +44 (0)191 261 1585

London Region
English Heritage
Greater London Archaeology Advisory
Service (GLAAS)
1 Waterhouse Square
138-142 Holborn
London
EC1 2ST
Tel: +44 (0)20 7973 3000
Website:
<http://www.english-heritage.org.uk>

North West Region
Canada House
3 Chepstow Street
Manchester
M1 5FW
Tel: +44 (0)161 242 1400

East of England Region
Brooklands,
24 Brooklands Avenue
Cambridge
CB2 8BU
Tel: +44 (0)1223 582700

Yorkshire Region
37 Tanner Row
York
YO1 6WP
Tel: +44 (0)1904 601901

South West Region
29 Queen Square
Bristol
BS1 4ND
Tel: +44 (0)117 975 0700

East Midlands Region
44 Derngate
Northampton
NN1 1UH
Tel: +44 (0)1604 735400

South East Region
Eastgate Court
195-205 High Street
Guildford
GU1 3EH
Tel: +44 (0)1483 252000

West Midlands Region
112 Colmore Row
Birmingham
B3 3AG
Tel: +44 (0)121 625 6820

Historic Scotland

Head Office
Historic Scotland
Longmore House
Salisbury Place
Edinburgh
EH9 1SH
Tel: +44 (0)131 668 8600
Website:
<http://www.historic-scotland.gov.uk>

Scheduled Monument consents team
Tel: +44 (0)131 668 8770
Email: hs.inspectorate@scotland.gsi.gov.uk

Listed building consents team
Tel: +44 (0)131 668 8981/8717
Email: hs.inspectorate@scotland.gsi.gov.uk

Archaeology Programmes and Grants
Advice team
Tel: +44 (0)131 668 8650
Email: hs.inspectorate@scotland.gsi.gov.uk

Policy enquiries
Tel: +44 (0)131 668 8985
Email: hs.policy@scotland.gsi.gov.uk

Northern Ireland Environment Agency

Built Heritage General Enquiries
Built Heritage general enquiries
Tel: +44 (0)28 9054 3095
Email: bh@doeni.gov.uk

Historic Buildings general enquiries
Tel: +44 (0)28 9054 3095
Email: historicbuildings@doeni.gov.uk

Monuments and Buildings Record
Tel: +44(0)28 9054 3004
Email: mbr@doeni.gov.uk

Archaeology and development